Emotional Logic

Harnessing your emotions into inner strength

Dr Trevor Griffiths and Dr Marian Langsford

BOOKS

Hammersmith Health Books
London, UK

First published in 2021 by Hammersmith Health Books
– an imprint of Hammersmith Books Limited
4/4A Bloomsbury Square, London WC1A 2RP, UK
www.hammersmithbooks.co.uk

British Library Cataloguing in Publication Data: A CIP record of this book is available from the British Library.

Print ISBN 978-1-78161-182-1
Ebook ISBN 978-1-78161-183-8

Commissioning editor: Georgina Bentliff
Designed and typeset by: Julie Bennett of Bespoke Publishing Ltd
Cover design by: Madeline Meckiffe
Cover image: © Lorna Roberts/Shutterstock
Index: Dr Laurence Errington
Production: Deborah Wehner of Moatvale Press Ltd
Printed and bound by: Ashford Colour Press, UK

Contents

List of illustrations

About the authors

Trevor Griffiths studied medicine at Oxford University. He was a pioneering GP for 25 years, introducing counsellors and family therapy into his practice. For the last 15 years he has run the Emotional Logic Centre full-time instead, training Emotional Logic coaches in the UK and around the world to prevent mental illness and socially disruptive behaviour, not just to treat it.

Marian Langsford is married to Trevor. She studied medicine at the Royal Free, London, and has used and researched Emotional Logic extensively in the medical practice they set up together. Now retired, she has joined Trevor in the international teaching of Emotional Logic, as well as enjoying their four grandchildren and cultivating their garden. As she says, 'Planting flowers that grow is more important than just pulling up weeds'.

To our daughters, sons-in-law, and grandchildren,
free and beautiful and strong.

And to the patients and families who have shared their stories.

Introducing Emotional Logic
– the missing link

As we write the world is in the grip of the Covid-19 pandemic. Life has changed dramatically for almost the whole of humankind, unexpectedly, instantly, unimaginably, shockingly. All of us have lost so much of that which we took for granted – normal life as we knew it.

All of those losses generate emotions. What emotions have you experienced, and which are you now experiencing? The loss emotions are not comfortable. Shock, Denial, Anger, Guilt, Yearning, Depression and even the sadness in Acceptance are not easy to live with. Why then are they part of our human experience? Could you imagine that they are part of our survival mechanism? How could Anger, for example, have a useful purpose in the context of the grief of loss of normality?

In this book we will demonstrate that the uncomfortable emotions of loss are inbuilt to help us keep moving through the process of adjustment to change until we find joy in a new future. Our natural state is to want to ignore these emotions and to calm ourselves down, but we can use our emotions to help us think logically again. You will soon be able to recognise, embrace and learn from both your own unpleasant emotions, and from the discomfort of sharing someone else's. From chaos, clarity can emerge that empowers renewed life after change has pushed us out of our comfort zones.

Life will never be 'normal' as it was in 2019, but we can embrace the new wholeheartedly if we have been able to truly, fully process the losses that have been inevitable. As two medical doctors, we understand how loss emotions build up into stress and can harm physical health, prevent healing, bring on mental distress, and disrupt previously stable relationships. Emotions are physical. They affect the way every cell of the body works and connects responsively with other cells, or disconnects chemically and becomes isolated, unresponsive and unhealthy. However, by welcoming the insights your emotions bring you about the values that make you *uniquely you*, not only will your physical health improve, but also your relationships with others will simultaneously transform, and life will begin to make more sense.

This book in your hands is going to open your eyes to a new way to map your inner emotional landscape, your 'inscape', so that you can harness your unpleasant and perhaps disturbing emotional energy into constructive action plans. With these, and with learning a new language of emotions to make sense of them with others, you can navigate your way through situations and come through stronger than when you set out on the journey. We have been teaching this for 18 years, enabling people of all ages to no longer feel victims of their emotions, but to be masters of them instead. Thousands of people worldwide have learnt to activate their inner Emotional Logic, so we *know* that our teaching on loss emotions activates their ability to adapt and transform life, and to move on with a reasonable hope.

The lifelong learning method we use to activate your Emotional Logic is not therapy. Improving understanding about how a healthy adjustment process might get stuck, releases your emotional energy to get life unstuck again and move on, rather than remaining passive, or only mindful of your emotions. It gives you a mental framework to engage constructively with life in all its unpredictability, especially after setbacks and disappointments. The method gives you the inner clarity to talk with confidence about your values in your home, with neighbours and friends, teachers and work colleagues. Emotional Logic's method has been translated into 10 languages and is used on four continents. It engages with personal truth in a liberating way at a deeper level than any culture or language. It releases human nature to adapt and adjust to changing life circumstances by building life-enhancing connections that overcome unhelpful modes of thinking, behaving and relating.

Every unpleasant emotion you have gains a new meaning when you see how it fits within a single, integrated, healthy process of adjusting to the losses hidden within change, disappointment, setback and hurt. We say surprisingly that there are no negative emotions, only unpleasant ones that have useful purposes. If you knew how to harness them into your inner strength, the unpleasant emotions would evaporate as you become more effective in life. There are negative self-beliefs and negative beliefs about the world. These lead to negative thoughts and broken relationships.

Unpleasant loss emotions, however, only lead to negative behaviour when their useful purposes are misunderstood. Learning to activate your Emotional Logic whenever you face new challenging situations will harness that emotional energy *on the instant* for healthy adjustment.

Many people feel that mindful calming doesn't go anywhere and leaves them dangling, while only regulating behaviour and thoughts simply ignores the heart of being human. The gap between these two approaches to life's challenges is filled by Emotional Logic's awareness and energising of active choice in social settings. This is the missing link that harnesses into *solution-focused action plans* your new understanding that unpleasant emotions have useful purposes.

In the first part of this book there are nine stories that Marian would like to share, eight of them from people who were so helped in her medical practice that they are happy to share the anonymised details of their emotional patterns and reactions. We have discovered certain patterns of emotional response to loss that could move anyone predictably into behaviours and inner drives that can be diagnosed as common mental illnesses or socially disruptive personalities. But we are able to show how underneath those labels are unhelpful patterns of grieving for lost values. These *emotional habits* can be re-learnt, resulting in the personal development of a stronger identity.

Marian has kindly given her consent for me to add some explanatory comments to her stories, so that you can learn how to unlearn any habits you discover in yourself.

In the second part of the book, following Marian's Emotional Logic Casebook, I tell some stories about how Emotional Logic has impacted communities. Shockingly, conflict, neglect, abuse, and crime, are all emotional dynamics just as much as compassion, kindness, love and hope. In schools, however, about 50% of teachers resist teaching emotional literacy, thinking it is all 'touchy feely, cotton wool cuddly' pandering, when what is really needed, they believe, is discipline to regulate behaviour and keep children on the curriculum. Emotional Logic fills the gap between these two extremes. Self-respect and self-discipline grow from improved understanding, as these later stories show. They aim to restore hope when the society we live in is under strain.

Before you read any of the 'cases', I need to introduce you to some of the diagrams that Marian shares with her patients, otherwise they will come as a surprise and only baffle you. They illustrate an overall adjustment process that brings your emotional energy and your reasoned planning into a creative partnership, called *your Emotional Logic*. Our schools team has developed the equivalent age-appropriate materials for children aged from 4 years onwards, through the transition to secondary (high) school and beyond into adult life and parenting. There will not be space to show most of the children's materials here (but there are examples in Chapters 3 and 14, and in the Appendix), so I shall simply say, 'They work!' Children learn; parents are amazed; teachers relax.

Our big overview of the constant movement of *life* is shown in Figure 0.1, in a diagram that we call *the Life Cycle*. Some people prefer to call it an 'emotional cycle' or an 'emotional awareness diagram'. It does not matter which name you use.

YOU ONLY GRIEVE IF YOU HAVE LOVED
THAT HONOURS YOU AND OTHERS AS HUMAN BEINGS

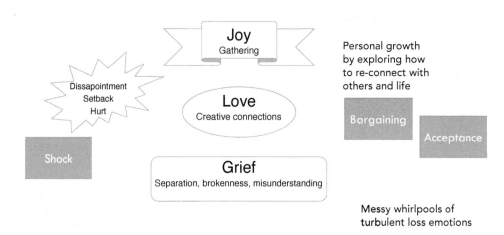

Figure 0.1 – The Life Cycle diagram

Whichever name you prefer, the point of this diagram is that life is about movement. Energy transforms and re-organises life. Your Emotional Logic helps you to restore movement when your life feels frustratingly stuck. E-motion = energy in motion.

The survival purposes of your unpleasant loss emotions are not fulfilled by just 'staying with' the *feelings of emotion* that preoccupy your mind. That creates a state of passivity, which leaves some people disengaged from a changing world. There is nothing wrong with calming, but we need to move on from there to know how to engage safely and actively with some unpredictability in the world.

From a medical doctor's point of view, emotion is physical, and it sends out social messages that others can understand. It is your body and brain's way of preparing you for action to connect with or step back from situations. *Feelings* of emotion, however, are the evidence of bodily emotion in your consciousness. They are very individual depending on your upbringing and memories. Wisely understood, your physical emotion connects you into the changing world of possibilities. It equips you to interact with fellow creatures, human and animal, with insight into what is likely to happen next because of the way they and you are similarly emotionally primed and communicating.

For this reason, whenever we talk about a physical emotion in Emotional Logic we shall give the name a capital letter as a proper noun, to indicate that it is a firm inner state of preparation with a meaning and useful purpose that moves an adjustment reaction forward. If we are referring to a feeling of emotion, however, it will have a lower case letter. So, Anger is a Stepping Stone that surprisingly can help adjustment processes along, while anger is a feeling that people often worry about.

The Life Cycle revolves around what is important, around personal values. It revolves around what we love, and who we love and what we hate and how we respond to each other. The details of this diagram will be explained through the stories. For now, the point to remember is this. Grief is not the end of love. Love in its widest sense of enduring, life-giving responsiveness has simply shifted to a different mode, from its joy mode to its 'you need to work out what to do to preserve this' mode. The grief emotions of bereavement are the same physically as those that arise during everyday setbacks and disappointments. While honouring the intense grieving of bereavement when someone close has died, this book is mainly about the way small, multiple everyday losses can accumulate over time into an overwhelming state of turmoil that can feel like a bereavement. When change pushes people out of a comfort zone, the many loss reaction emotions that together are known as grief are *purposely uncomfortable* in order to shift us all into action. Their purpose is to *move us* to do something wise that restores the joy of love. We are not supposed to stay with them. We are supposed to harness them.

Getting to the top right hand corner of this Life Cycle diagram is the aim of activating your inbuilt Emotional Logic. Once the joy of connection is rediscovered, as shown at the top of the diagram, your life is an open door. On walking through it, all life's beauty and creativity and pleasant emotion can flourish. Emotional Logic is that door. Some people call it a fire escape, always there for when you need it.

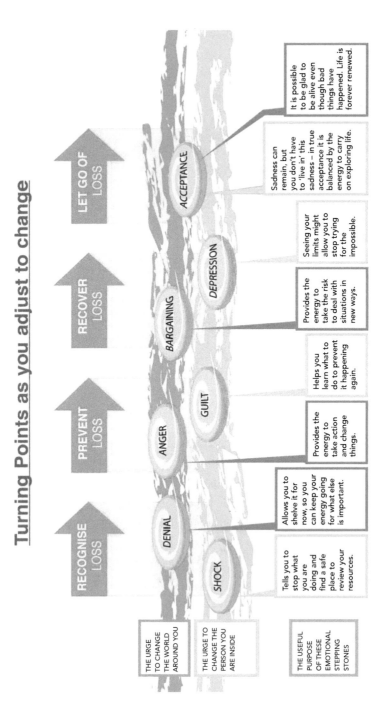

Figure 0.2 – The Turning Points diagram

*

The lower half of the Life Cycle diagram, from Shock to Bargaining and Acceptance, is expanded into the Turning Points diagram, shown in Figure 0.2. This can be used to demonstrate why people sometimes get stuck in this lower half of the cycle, in 'grief for everyday losses', and how it is possible to move on from that sense of 'stuckness'.

This diagram shows the useful purposes of seven core emotional states that together make a single, healthy, physical adjustment process. But it is only theory! Life is *never* like that. The stories will make that clear. By teaching a healthy adjustment process we aim to restore a realistic hope that life *can be renewed*. We are not asking you to squeeze your life into this adjustment shape. Part of the beauty of Emotional Logic is that it recognises, honours and enhances human diversity. We all react differently to situations according to our personal values. By understanding the healthy adjustment process, people are simply less likely to get stuck in the unpleasant bits 'telling themselves off' or criticising themselves and others inappropriately. By knowing where they and others are *in the process*, people can make better choices about how to move on.

The four arrows across the top of Figure 0.2 are the 'Turning Points' of a healthy adjustment process. They show how you can *turn to face a situation* with that purpose in mind to get yourself organised. These four purposes are the *Logic* of Emotional Logic. Adjusting is a logical process. You can decide where you want to be in it when focusing your mind on managing a named loss. You can also choose how best to harness your emotional energy for the purpose you have in mind, either by preparing to go out into the world to change something there, or by looking in to see if you can change something in your own inner heart. Both are equally important life skills.

One final feature of the Turning Points diagram to notice is the line of text boxes along the bottom that summarise the useful purpose of each of the loss emotions. These purposes may come as a surprise, and are worth trying to remember. For example, many people worry that their shock feelings mean they are weak, but we say they are the vital message that something you value is at risk. You need to stop what you are doing, and find a safe place to work out what is going on. If you know this, the feelings of shock turn instead into a firm inner place for adjustment, an emotional Stepping Stone called Shock that alerts you to an action. You will discover that the Emotional Logic idea of a safe place is mentioned in many of the stories. It is not like a bomb shelter to hide in, but your planning office to work out how to re-emerge and move on with life more effectively. We have something constructive like that to say about every unpleasant loss emotion.

However, because we are human beings, we never go through an emotional adjustment process in such a logically organised way as shown in the Turning Points diagram. Marian and I therefore made sets of seven cards that represent the core emotional adjustment states, and we called them 'Stepping Stones cards', as shown in Figure 0.3. These keep you safely away from the idea that there are 'stages' to the adjustment process. That word 'stages' unhelpfully suggests that there might be a 'right' sequence, and if you miss one you ought to go back and do it… No! Healthy adjustment to everyday setbacks and disappointments is much more flexible than that.

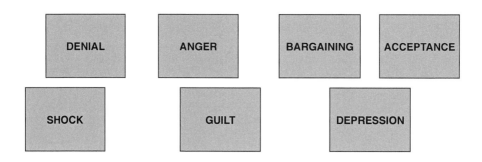

Figure 0.3 – Emotional Stepping Stones cards

Some people jump all over the place emotionally; others get stuck with one or two of the helpful emotional states and dare not access the others. The imagery of using stepping stones to cross a shallow river became a theme, a metaphor, which you will repeatedly come across in this book. The river is the constantly changing flow of life. With a bit of careful thought and physical effort, you can leap from any emotional Stepping Stone to another to get where you want to be to restore some joy to life in a situation – even if some sadness remains about what you have had to leave behind to get there.

We ask people to sort the cards into a pattern that represents how they feel inside when remembering a particular situation in which they had felt stuck or upset, or had been made to adjust.

Let's try an example. Imagine yourself in this scenario. During the post-Covid recovery era you are in a shop, and you are selecting items off a shelf to put them into your basket. An employee of the store approaches you, and in an abrupt manner loudly tells you off for not wearing a mask. How do you feel?

I might lay down:

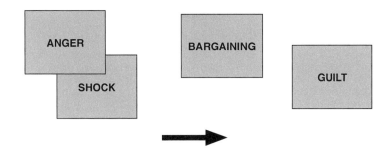

You might lay down:

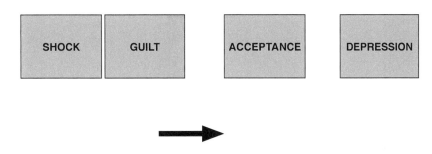

Figure 0.4 (a) and (b) – Possible responses to being told off

Or you might lay down any of an infinite range of patterns. There is no right or wrong – only an opportunity to be honest… Have a go with our online card-pattern generator some time. (See the Appendix for further learning resources.) The point of showing the two example emotional card patterns (Figure 0.4) is that our physical reactions to that staff member would be different. We have found over the years, from working with thousands of people and situations, that people's behavioural reactions can be associated *predictively* with their *patterns* of loss emotions in situations. Our inner emotional states are complex, but they can be mapped safely using Emotional Logic's toolkit, and that increases our powers of insight and choice.

In that toolkit we have an extra set of 28 small green cards with the names of feelings of emotion that can add even greater insight to the Stepping Stones card patterns. You'll see these used in Chapter 5. There are extensive 'Naming Feelings' lists also in the Appendix to help people broaden their range of vocabulary to describe how they feel, and to connect these feelings to the useful purposes of the emotional Stepping Stones they are associated with.

A significant discovery of Emotional Logic is the range of consequences that follows predictively when *two* strong emotions occur at the same time. We call this a 'whirlpool of loss emotions', or an 'entanglement'. Neither of the emotions can then fulfil its useful purpose. Instead, distress, tension, or confusion build up. The clue to this feature of loss reactions in Figure 0.4 is the overlapping or touching cards. A summary sheet of common whirlpools of loss emotions can be found in the Appendix (page 164). They do not inevitably have the effects listed there, but if someone has those effects, then a bit of learning about the useful purposes of the two component emotions can set people free.

You will see from the stories that follow, however, how a wide range of unique patterns becomes the starting place for learning about a healthy adjustment process. Simply understanding the useful purposes of unpleasant loss emotions can spontaneously untangle various unhelpful snags in people's patterns of adjustment.

There are two more Emotional Logic 'tools' that you will see mentioned by Marian in her Casebook. The Loss Reaction Worksheet is 'the powerhouse for change'. An example is shown in Figure 0.5.

We build up a list of previously un-named 'hidden losses' as someone is telling the story of their situation. This example is for someone who was made redundant from their work. We then check with the person if the guesses we have made seem true. In this way people learn to be more reflective about their personal values. You only know what you value when you see a risk that you might lose it. In a hard-copy Loss Reaction Worksheet, such as the one shown here, the situation is written as a heading above this grid. There is an online version also, screenshots of which are shown associated with Marian's Casebook (page 48).

Basically, by building up this list of *hidden losses* in this situation, and asking the person to tick the emotions they feel about each one, we can map as a 'tick pattern' the inner tension of the person's heart, which drives his or her behavioural reaction whenever he or she remembers the situation. This opens new options to agree action plans that recover *just one* of the hidden losses. The *Emotional Logic*

NAMED LOSSES	SHOCK	DENIAL	ANGER	GUILT	BARG'N	DEPR'N	ACCEPT
job (made redundant)	✓		✓			✓	
pride			✓			✓	
meeting friends			✓				
routine						✓	
reason to get up			✓			✓	
wife's respect	✓			✓			
gym membership			✓			✓	
money	✓		✓			✓	
independence			✓			✓	
interest in life						✓	
direction			✓			✓	
peace at home						✓	
self-respect			✓	✓		✓	

Figure 0.5 – The Loss Reaction Worksheet

strategy described here starts a rippling *Butterfly Effect* that improves self-respect and releases more personal energy to reshape life. A Butterfly Effect means here that a small change in the way someone understands the purpose of even one unpleasant emotion in a healthy adjustment process can have a huge impact on their behaviour and relationships. Such is the empowerment from the 'Emotional Chaos Theory' that lies behind the practical tools of Emotional Logic. If you become interested in how personal inner and social order can emerge from emotional overload, there is more on my essay site, www.relatedness.net.

Finally, we have a diagram that explains how there is a useful purpose even for the 'Depression of loss' as part of our survival toolkit. We call this the 'Growth Cycle roundabout', shown in Figure 0.6. The Depression of loss is not clinical depression. It can turn into clinical depression if it gets entangled into whirlpools, but if it gets restored to its rightful place in the Growth Cycle this can help to release people from clinical depression. Marian's stories show how understanding the useful purpose of emptiness and powerlessness can even *prevent* clinical depression, when people can recognise those feelings as a *place of decision* in a healthy adjustment process.

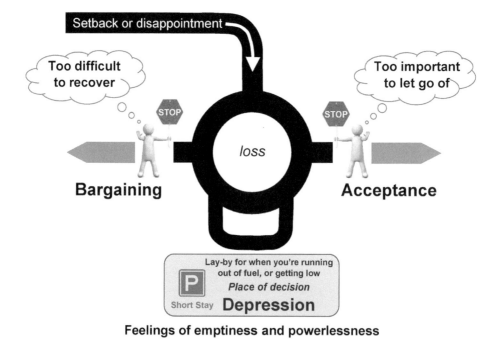

Figure 0.6 – The Growth Cycle roundabout

In summary, to activate your inbuilt Emotional Logic:
(a)   map and make sense of your emotional experience
(b)   name the hidden personal losses that shape your emotional landscape and the Stepping Stones that you are using to adjust

(c) recognise that those named losses are in fact *your personal values* – your personal identity reacting in the world

(d) make a wise action plan to recover *just one* of your personal values as a way to grow stronger through the situation.

These steps are illustrated throughout this book.

*

So, to conclude, if anyone asks you, 'What *is* Emotional Logic?' you could try replying with our definition:

> Your Emotional Logic is your inbuilt capacity for one emotion to evolve constructively into another as you prepare in different ways to adjust to the personal losses hidden within change.

However, most people find that brief summary a bit too intense. It's actually quite difficult to explain Emotional Logic in a few words, and the reason for that is quite beautiful. It is because physically *moving* the emotional Stepping Stones cards around, either with hard copy cards or online, until the pattern intuitively matches how you feel as you remember a situation, gets deeper into the truth of your human nature than any language.

Part 1

Dr Marian's Emotional Logic casebook

Nine stories introduce the emotion mapping tools that we use in Emotional Logic. Marian might recognise problems during her 10-minute General Practice surgery appointments and then invite patients back to a long appointment, where a *lifelong learning conversation* can continue with less pressure. The stories go on to show how these conversations lead to important insights about personal values and action plans that can improve health and relationships by generating renewed inner strength and stability. Studies conducted over several years have shown that GP consultation rates and prescribing have reduced as a consequence of this time investment in learning. The original meaning of 'Doctor' is 'Teacher'. We just enjoy being old-fashioned!

Chapter 1

The way I use Emotional Logic for myself

Marian's garden

I love Autumn as a 'season of mellow fruitfulness'. Along with the fruit harvesting, I like to bring some colour into the house to last through the Winter and remind me of Summer. Hydrangea heads keep their colour well when dried, and I had spotted some rather splendid ones beside the drive.

A friend offered to help tidy my overgrown end-of-Summer garden. She could blow some leaves off our drive, she said, and maybe clear back its edges. A little later, as we'd agreed, I set off on an errand. At this point I noticed her pruning a bush. I thought, 'That's opening up a view.' Then in a sudden state of shock I realised, 'Oh, no! All those beautiful mauve and lime green hydrangea flowers have gone! They've been cut off!'

'Where are the hydrangeas?' I asked. 'Oh,' she replied, 'Did you want them?' (looking at the recycling bin rammed full of them). 'I think you've got some more in the back garden.'

But I knew those were boring colours. I replied, 'Oh, no. Don't worry.' And I drove off.

In emotional turmoil now, I thought, 'I had better take care with my driving. As my mother would have said, "I am in charge of a lethal weapon". This seems to have gone deeper than I might expect. So, yes, be honest, I'm in Shock.'

'How am I going to cope with this disappointment?' It seemed like a small thing, but even small things grow sometimes, like weeds. Quickly, a tinge of Guilt (my favourite Stepping Stone) popped up. I should have picked some the other day when we got back from the dog walk and I had mentioned them to Trevor. He had said at the time, 'Are you going to bring them in now?' I had been too anxious for a cup of tea, and said, 'I'll get some later'. Now it was too late. My fault! Could I have done something different? Yes, but I had had no reason to rush. So, no – not really. How could I have known she was going to hack them all off, apparently without a thought? 'Actually, now I am really angry!'

I needed to complete the errands I had set out on. 'I had better focus. Put the disappointment into Denial. Keep my energy for driving safely and for ticking these tasks off my list. That usually makes me feel better.' Not that day, though. Taking Skye-dog for her customary walk on the way back from the errands, I was steamingly angry! A bit over the top? It crossed my mind that perhaps I was still grieving for that ancient Red American oak tree that the Council had to fell just across from our garden? And then our neighbour's lovely clematis blew over in that storm. What a disappointment that had been! Perhaps these hydrangea flower heads were just 'the last straw' in a difficult Summer?

So, I reasoned, 'My anger is meant to be about trying to prevent loss. I know it's supposed to give me energy to change something out there, something external. But I cannot *prevent* this loss! It's gone already. I am powerless over it. In fact, I am powerless over everything, it now seems'. As I trudged through the mud, I was feeling empty and pointless, with my dog having disappeared, and I no longer cared. Before long, the anger feelings and my depressive emptiness began to twist around each other. I was starting to feel vindictive.

Fortunately, I then remembered that I knew Emotional Logic. I started to reason that there were two ways out of this unhappy state. I could *Bargain* to try to get something back, or I could *Accept* the loss and let go of my dreams. I found myself looking into the recycling bin on the way back home to see if any of the hydrangea heads were salvageable. No, they were now crushed under twiggy rubbish; so *that* Bargaining gambit failed! 'Did she miss any, before I go in?' Only some battered ones near the ground.

I now started to reason this out properly. *Assertive Bargaining*, the best way of attempting to recover things, would involve teaming up, negotiating, discussing, naming what is important to me and stating it simply. I should ask my friend to check with me along the way, if she is going to help again in the garden. But I know she was genuinely trying to be helpful, because she knew that I had become exceptionally busy. That sort of conversation could prevent further loss, though. It might help me to recover my sense of effectiveness.

However, in my state of mind at the time that felt like hard work. She wasn't there when I came back in. That seemed a relief, which was a bit sad in itself. I would do it next week. Meanwhile, I found myself Accepting that I had to let go of those mauve and lime flowers, for this year anyway. 'I may feel empty for now, but I can at least decide *something*, and that is… I am going to Bargain assertively for next year, to influence what happens then.'

'Do I text her to thank her for the good things she did?' I still felt a hint of temptation to text her about the one thing that had upset me. 'Or should I just stay silent?' I felt empty and powerless *again*, going around and around. 'Oh no! Time for a cup of tea. That's one of my safe places. Perhaps I'll feel strong enough when I've had time for a think. I need to think about what's really important here. Friendship *is* more important. I'm sure we need to meet again soon, and I'll find a way to say it. Even though it feels risky, it is too important to avoid. So, what am I worried I might lose if she takes it the wrong way? Better make a Plan B so I don't over-react if *she* gets upset! Let's start by naming what's important to me. It might be that she finds the same things are important to her.'

Will Trevor give the time to listen?

It took me a few decades to realise that it did me a lot of good to listen to Marian. I think many men discover the same at some point in their married lives...

As the eldest daughter in a Devon farming family, Marian grew up on a mixed dairy and horticulture farm overlooking rolling hills, surrounded by buckets of early flowers that needed bunching each evening for market the next day. They were not rich. She loved it. She has a wisdom from nature that I had missed, having been brought up in the London suburbs. For example, she once said, 'Gardening isn't all about pulling up weeds. You have to plant something in the earth in its place, and care for it.' A comment like that can leave me fixed into a garden chair for ages while I watch her getting her hands covered in earth and planting. Something simple like this can lead me to a lot of thinking, which I consider to be my core skill.

So, what do I think about? I think a lot about human nature. I think things like, 'Seemingly small things that break out on the surface of people's lives can have deeper roots than we realise at first'.

I remain fascinated by the way the body tends to heal when it has been injured – but not always, and usually not perfectly. And likewise, I am fascinated by the way a person's inner emotional heart tends to heal with time – but not always, and not perfectly. My decades of thinking about 'healing' could be summarised in Marian's comment about gardening, however. It isn't all about pulling up weeds, or disinfecting against germs, or pulling out bits of debris (physically or psychologically) that have got under the skin. It isn't all about removing root causes. You need to plant a seed of something strong and growing into human nature as well, and care for it.

That's what Emotional Logic is about – planting seeds that can grow into something strong, and something beautiful.

Marian, did you notice, only properly activated her Emotional Logic knowledge when it struck her that her emotions were getting out of proportion to the situation. They were winding up into something potentially destructive. Some weeds were getting in there, entangling her and blocking her way forward. She was getting stuck with her emotions, rather than harnessing their energy to face and handle the situation constructively, which is what they are there for. Unpleasant emotions are built into us for useful purposes, not just to spoil life. Emotional Logic shows how to make sense of them, and not become victims of them.

All those unpleasant feelings of emotion had their roots in the loss of her hopes to bring the beauty of these flowers into our home. Those emotions were growing before she realised that they had activated memories of other losses. Shock, guilty self-questioning, anger and a sense of powerlessness grew until they added a further round of empty, depressive feelings. Up to that point, she had not seen in those emotions anything other than normal, healthy living. That's what it is to have a friendship in which a disappointment disturbs the peace. But when it starts winding up... That was the clue that her emotions were no longer fulfilling their natural in-built useful purposes.

Unpleasant emotions are built into our genetics to energise appropriate mini-adjustments of behaviour during life's daily situations. The same emotional preparations are available to help us manage the big disruptions to life as well. It all revolves around what's important to us – around our personal values.

I use the Life Cycle diagram, mentioned in the Introduction and shown here in Figure 1.1, to help people picture how their in-built Emotional Logic fits into a healthy way of facing everyday setbacks and disappointments.

Life revolves around what people value, which is another way of saying what they

YOU ONLY GRIEVE IF YOU HAVE LOVED
THAT HONOURS YOU AND OTHERS AS HUMAN BEINGS

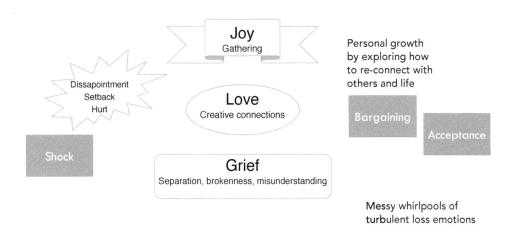

Figure 1.1 – The Life Cycle diagram

love. Perhaps life ought to revolve around what they need, but it is amazing how people can disregard their needs when some other pleasure catches their attention. When love, in its broadest sense of creative connection, is going well there is joy or happiness on gathering together with the people and things loved and valued. To many, this is what love is. When disappointments, setbacks or hurts arise, joy breaks down into grief for everyday situations (not only on bereavement), and a strange idea can arise that this is now the end of love. But it isn't!

The truth is that love has only transformed into a different mode. You only grieve if you have loved. And that grief has a purpose, which is to restore the connection and responsiveness that are the essence of loved values. This purpose gets obscured when people think that grieving means only bereavement, when the person who has died is not going to return. In fact, a sense of connection and responsiveness with valued *aspects* of that person's life can still be recovered through memorial actions that honour what has gone. And in everyday losses and setbacks, the joy of gathering *can* sometimes be restored. For Marian, bringing flowers into the home restores connection with her whole history and upbringing, embedded in her values. Would it help if I went out and bought her a bouquet of flowers? It would address some, but not all, of the values being challenged here.

Relatedness can be strained by separation, brokenness or misunderstanding. These can activate a healthy adjustment process, from Shock, as people doubt their abilities or resources to handle a situation, via several unpleasant emotions, all with unique useful purposes, to a choice between Bargaining and Acceptance, where people explore new ways to reconnect with their values. We call these your 'growth points' within grieving. They lead to action plans or inner transformations that restore the potential for joy to be restored, by improved responsiveness with others, or managing a healthy distance from those it is wise not to interact with.

The seven emotional Stepping Stones cards that map a healthy or stuck adjustment process (Figure 1.2, first described in the Introduction) can be sorted into patterns on a table or lap tray. Powerful as these card patterns are in learning how to unlock emotional tension or distress or confusion, the healthy emotional Life Cycle is only completed when a personal value has been restored, so that the grief mode returns to joy. Learning from the card patterns helps to release the emotional energy needed to bring this about.

Most of us will have heard someone say something along the lines of 'I've been through a terrible time, and I couldn't wish that on anyone, but I've come through it stronger'. Learning to activate your Emotional Logic makes sense of how grief's unpleasant feelings connect into paths that lead to growth points.

There is a problem, however. Cycles of healthy adjustment can happen several times a day, but commonly may get stuck half way around. The unpleasant feelings that come with grieving may stop people from thinking clearly, or from seeing their way through to their growth points. People may become overwhelmed into a sense of isolation. When others seem unaffected, it is difficult to know how to communicate sometimes.

The following chapters explore how to reconnect and get life unstuck when states of isolation have built up. In Marian's story, she recognised that her distress and tension were building up. She found a 'safe place', her cup of tea. It would have helped her to slow down and start naming a few of the things she valued. She mentioned a few along the way that we could guess: finding a reasonable way to talk with a friend; the beauty of nature in her home; trees growing near her garden; completing tasks; the time her friend gave her to catch up with herself; ticking things off her list; her sense of effectiveness; caring for her pet dog's wellbeing; driving safely; her mother's advice; a cup of tea…

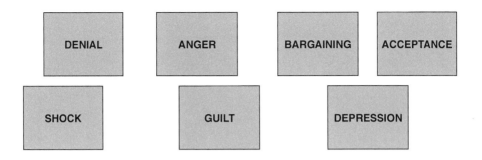

Figure 1.2 – Emotional Stepping Stones cards

Are you beginning to get a picture of who Marian is? Her unpleasant loss emotions were not part of the problem. They were not 'negative emotions'. They were the grieving Marian. They are vital clues to her values, on which the future strength and beauty of her life will depend. Emotional Logic equips people to tune in to values, and then to find joy in teaming up to plan some action that is likely to build a future on them.

Chapter 2

Chris and Peter resolve a conflict

Marian tells the story

Christine 'I prefer to be called Chris' and Peter came to learn Emotional Logic. Chris had arranged the appointment, saying that their marriage was at risk. She was worried also that the conflict at home was upsetting their 13-year-old twin girls.

Chris introduced the problem by saying that for the past six weeks her important work had caused her to be away during the week, attending 'think tank' meetings. She came home every – well, almost every – weekend, and she made sure there were meals in the freezer, and the girls' school uniforms were ready for Monday, before leaving again on the Sunday evening. So, she felt she didn't deserve the sense of betrayal she was picking up from the family. Peter remained quiet and seemed unengaged.

Chris was keen to continue telling her side of the story, but I felt Peter needed to be heard too. Therefore, to keep this all in a lifelong-learning mode, I handed them each a set of orange emotional Stepping Stones cards and explained that they represent the main emotions associated with a disappointment or loss. We can use them to say to people, 'Don't *tell* me how you feel about this situation; use these cards instead to *show* me'.

I suggested, 'Think of a small but difficult event in the last two weeks that was a bit of a disappointment or upset', and I set the usual 'rules'. These are: 'Use the cards to show intuitively how you felt during that time. You don't have to use all the cards. There is no right or wrong. What you lay down is the reality for you, as we are all different.'

Chris quickly suggested they both put down the Stepping Stone cards for, 'When I lost it, and broke that wine glass last Saturday'. I was about to say that it was not necessary to choose the same scenario, but Peter became more animated and agreed that was a good idea. Figure 2.1 shows the patterns they laid down.

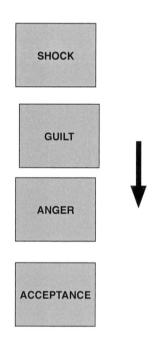

Figure 2.1 (a) Chris's card pattern

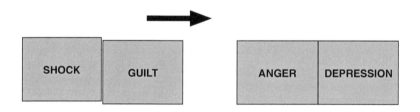

Figure 2.1 (b) Peter's card pattern

I was just making a mental note of the significant differences between these two patterns when Peter, looking at Chris' pattern, suddenly said, 'I don't believe you can accept that! It was my Grandmother's glass, a family heirloom, the only one left in the set, and you deliberately smashed it just to upset me!'

Chris looked away, becoming tearful. 'It wasn't deliberate. I didn't mean to lose my temper. I can't remake it, so I just have to accept it.'

Already, as is my usual way, I had been making guesses as to what they might have lost, and was writing them on two Loss Reaction Worksheets – one for each. On Peter's I had 'family heirloom', '?memory of Grandma', as well as 'my possessions being valued', and 'respect from Chris'. Chris's list now included 'my temper' and 'self-control', adding to those from her introduction, 'being part of the family', and 'being valued'.

However, I needed to step in quickly here. This couple were conflicted and in danger of going off down a well-worn path. I pushed forward a copy of the Turning Points diagram (Figure 2.2, introduced in the Introduction) between them so that they both had to look at it, and by pointing at its features I started to explain an overview of grief as an adjustment process, from *Shock* about a loss to the growth points of *Bargaining* and *Acceptance* where we explore ways to grow stronger through adjusting constructively.

When I explained the useful purposes of true Acceptance, as exploring something new when letting go of something valued, we all agreed that what Chris had described was *not* that. It was more like *Denial*, putting the issue on a shelf partially unresolved in order to get on with something else. Nothing wrong with doing that, as long as you know you are doing it!

However, I wanted to quickly move on to teach them about the useful purpose of Shock. They both had placed Shock at the start of the adjustment sequence shown by the arrows in their patterns. That is a helpful place for it to be, but it is always a good idea to check that people understand how to turn the personal energy of Shock to its useful purpose. So, pointing that out, I suggested that they both turn over their Shock Stepping Stones cards and read the backs (Figure 2.3).

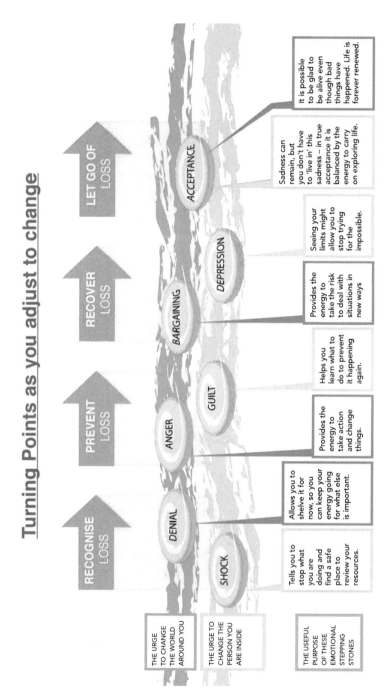

Figure 2.2 – Turning Points diagram

> **SHOCK**
>
> ***To adjust:***
> I need to recognise loss
> ***It means:***
> I am doubting my resources
> ***Useful purpose:*** Stop what you are doing!
> FInd a safe place to review your resources!

Figure 2.3 – Wording on the Shock card

Chris read aloud, 'I need to recognise loss. Meaning – I am doubting my resources. Useful purpose – Stop what you are doing, and find a safe place to review your resources'.

A moment of silence followed. Both were studying the backs of the Shock cards, re-reading and pondering this information. Eventually, it was Peter who spoke first.

'I am surprised. You never seem to doubt yourself; you are the self-confident one! I was the one who messed up the promotion interview by getting anxious.' I now added 'promotion', 'self-confidence' and 'self-esteem' to Peter's loss list. Chris replied, 'I have to put on that armour when I am at work, but I would rather just be me at home – if you would let me.' I added to her loss list guesses of 'feeling safe at work' as well as 'being allowed to be myself'.

I then explained about the three types of safe place that the feelings of shock can alert us to look for – a physical place, a mental frame and a relationship. I explained that an Emotional Logic safe place is not just a hideaway. It is a place to plan what to do about the situation. Asking Chris and Peter about their own safe places led to a shift in the atmosphere between them. Chris volunteered that safe places were in short supply at her work. She felt that her professionalism was a mind space she used a lot, but recognised now that she often needed to use Denial. She turned that Stepping Stones card over (and I noticed Peter follow suit). She read aloud, 'Shelve it for now, so I can carry on with what else is important'.

```
┌─────────────────────────────────────────┐
│              DENIAL                      │
│  To adjust:                              │
│  I need to recognise loss                │
│  It means:                               │
│  I can carry on regardless               │
│  Useful purpose: Shelve it for now, so I │
│  can keep my energy going for what else is│
│  important.                              │
└─────────────────────────────────────────┘
```

Figure 2.4 – Wording on the Denial card

'Yes,' she continued. 'The problem is there's too much on the shelf! I used to talk about work issues to my colleague and friend Carol, but I don't see her while I'm working away.' I wrote 'safe places' on Chris' loss list.

Peter, meanwhile, was quietly staring at the back of the Shock card and looking shocked too. He seemed unable to identify any safe places. I also added safe places to his list.

At this point there seemed to be a tipping point in the process. I decided to take a risk and asked Peter, 'What would it take for Chris to become a safe place for you?' He became very tearful. He said, 'She IS – always has been!'

At this, Chris reached out to take Peter's hand and she moved her chair closer so that her knee was touching his. Peter went on to affirm, 'You were so helpful and supportive when my Dad died two years ago; and when I didn't get that promotion, too. I really miss you when you are away so much!'

At this, Chris moved closer still and looked weepy, saying, 'I really miss you too – and the girls. I don't know how I will cope with the final two weeks of this work pattern. I was getting worried that I wouldn't have a marriage to come back to!'

Bargaining, and styles of Bargaining, seemed good topics to address next in this changed atmosphere. They had arrived at the place where they were emotionally prepared to look for solutions. Growth points are only effective when focused on how to manage one specific named loss within a situation, not the whole situation. Before sharing with Chris and Peter the loss lists that I had been guessing, I decided to check on their habitual way of trying to recover something they value – their preferred *style* of Bargaining.

I explained the differences between aggressive, passive and assertive styles of Bargaining, and showed them some word lists that we use as examples of these styles (see the Appendix, page 168). They recognised how aggressive and passive styles can both cause extra problems, and were clear that they both used assertive methods at work. However, Chris did own up that she tended to be aggressive on occasions at home, and Peter recognised that he tended to be passive outside of work, although in the broken glass situation he had used threats – an aggressive style. This struck a chord with me as I remembered Peter's emotional card pattern. He still had it on the table, and I was able to say that I could have foretold this aggressive response from his card pattern… He looked surprised and curious. I pointed to the Anger and Depression cards being very close together, if not touching.

ANGER	**DEPRESSION**
To adjust:	***To adjust:***
I need to prevent loss	I need to recover loss
It means:	***It means:***
I must stop this happening, or prevent it happening again.	I feel empty and powerless.
Useful purpose: It gives me energy to take action out in the world and change something there.	***Useful purpose:*** Recognising my limits might allow me to stop trying for the impossible.

Figure 2.5 – Wording on the Anger card

Figure 2.6 – Wording on the Depression card

'This feature of the pattern suggests that these two adjustment emotions may start to interfere with each other, so neither can fulfil its useful purpose properly. We call it a "whirlpool of loss emotions". Anyone whose loss reaction twists around like this between angry and depressive feelings could begin to feel *destructive*. It generates a desire to break up the situation, which could be quite out of character because it is driven by grief.'

Using the backs of the Stepping Stones cards, teaching followed on the meanings and useful purposes of Anger and Depression. On seeing the back of the Depression card, Chris now wondered if the feelings she had labelled as Acceptance were in fact Depression – a feeling of powerlessness over the situation. She recognised now how they might have come on the back of reaching her limits about coping with this work pattern.

> **ACCEPTANCE**
>
> ***To adjust:***
> I need to let go of...
> ***Sadness means:***
> I have limits, but that's OK. It makes me human like everyone else.
> ***Joy means:*** It still have energy to explore my limits. Life is forever renewed.

Figure 2.7 – Wording on the Acceptance card

There were lots of new insights being worked on. I felt we were getting close to exploring a way forward now. It was time to share the Loss Reaction Worksheets. As we say, these are the *powerhouse for change*.

Most of my guesses were acknowledged as true losses. Both Chris and Peter were surprised at the number and variety of disappointments that they were coping with. Could we find anything SMART – small and practical enough to be recovered in a short period of time with a high chance of success? (That is, is the named loss to be recovered Specific, Measurable, Achievable, Relevant and Time-framed?) What assertive methods of Bargaining could they use to recover just one of these losses?

The session concluded with Peter and Chris agreeing to team up to spend a few hours of quality time together each weekend for the next few weeks, and to be safe places for each other – perhaps going for a walk in a favourite spot.

They left hand in hand. I stayed and tidied up my Activity Pack.

Trevor reflects on what happened here

There are several reasons why handling the seven emotional Stepping Stones cards is a powerful way to start bringing about a change in the way people understand each other. I'll fill out those reasons over some of the following stories, but let's start here by looking at what Marian did.

Chris was keen to carry on telling her story, and perhaps to share more of her feelings about the situation, but Marian had noticed that Peter was quiet and seemed unengaged. One of Emotional Logic's many surprising claims is that the most fundamental of human needs is not, surprisingly, to be loved, but to be *heard*. From the first cry at birth to our dying breath, people hope that the response to being heard will be loving, but, even if it is not, hurt people not uncommonly return to abusive or oppressive relationships, perhaps because they are at least noticed there. For many people, being noticed is better than being ignored or abandoned. Offering Stepping Stones cards to people provides them with an alternative way to be heard without going back to old habitual ways.

Handling those Stepping Stones cards, and laying out a pattern for a remembered situation, intuitively *slows down* people's emotional reactions. It gets the inner emotional world 'out there' in a safe way. It can be seen and considered by the person and relevant others sitting side-by-side, without anyone looking another in the eye in a way that may seem intrusive or demanding. We call it a 'third dimension method', making visible externally and safely a person's inner heart. Any subsequent conversation is therefore informed by what people see, and this usually opens the door to enquiring further about the background story, so people then feel fully heard.

It worked! Peter noticed something unexpected about Chris's pattern that was highly significant for him. The conversation shifted onto a new track. Now they were starting to explore, but safely, because the emotional world that is otherwise so unpredictable and hidden was present openly between the two of them, with Marian also able to steer the mutual learning process.

Reading the backs of the cards keeps conversations on the theme of learning. The aim of an Emotional Logic conversation is to see how an unhealthy *pattern of grieving* might be contributing to a problem, and then to learn how a healthier adjustment reaction might contribute to solutions. The cards, information sheets and worksheets help to prevent the conversation from drifting in a counselling mode onto lengthy descriptions of feelings or behaviour. Instead, conversations rapidly go deeper, down through the world of feelings and reactions to insights that name personal values and empower solution-focused action plans. There are two more emotional Stepping Stones cards in the set as well as the five Marian taught from in that appointment. These are Bargaining and Guilt.

In the Turning Points diagram, Guilty self-questioning comes before Bargaining in a healthy adjustment process to recover something lost. Working out if there is anything that could be done differently could ideally be followed by getting on and doing it!

Marian showed Chris and Peter the Turning Points diagram to explain the overview of adjustment. The four arrows across the top show the Logic of Emotional Logic. As

GUILT
To adjust:
I need to prevent loss
It means:
I need to question if something I did caused it.
Useful purpose: Learning. Could I do something differently that might prevent it happening again?

BARGAINING
To adjust:
I need to recover loss
It means:
I must try doing something to get back what has gone.
Useful purpose: The energy to take risks to deal with new situations and other people in new ways.

Figure 2.8 – Wording on the Guilt card

Figure 2.9 – Wording on the Bargaining card

people turn to face a changing situation, they may adopt different frames of mind that see different features of the situation. Questions they may ask are:

- Firstly, can I recognise and name what I am worried I might lose in this situation?
- If so, then can I prevent that named loss? To do so requires a different frame of mind.
- If that named loss has gone from my control already, then can I turn again to look at this situation with a frame of mind to explore what I might do to get it back, or replace it?
- And if I have tried and failed to recover it, perhaps I could turn again to see what life might look like if I have to let go of it, exploring instead some new way to live without that important feature of my life?

That is a logical process of adjustment. People can make rational decisions about where they want to be in that process with regard to the losses hidden within change. The problem is that people mostly do not go through it logically! Mostly, people think more about what they want, so that on seeing a risk of loss they jump in at the 'prevent, prevent, prevent' Stepping Stones to try to control the situation without having first named any specific features of it that they are trying to prevent the loss of. This is why Marian was so keen to get the conversation back onto Shock and finding safe places to plan. In safe places, people can slow down their reactions and bring their thoughts and emotions into a partnership with a clearer purpose around named losses and values, before stepping out again into a risky and unpredictable world.

In an upside-down sort of a way, to ask 'What am I worried I might lose in this situation?' is a far more empowering question than 'What do I want to get out of this situation?'. In this story we may begin to see why. The core Emotional Logic questions about loss, or worry about loss, key into our true personal values more deeply. By naming what is truly important at a heart level, they connect mind and emotions in a truer picture of core personal identity. Asking what people want merely pushes mental buttons for pleasurable gain to motivate behaviour.

Because these core Emotional Logic questions do not come naturally to most people, Marian was jotting down her guesses about what Chris and Peter were losing right from the outset of their meeting. She thus had a good idea about what they were valuing before she shared her guesses, when the mood had changed and they were ready to start looking at solutions. It was out of agreeing these personal values that an action plan could be worked out. Emotional Logic is actually about the solution-focused action plan. Mapping the emotions at the outset of a conversation shows how to release trapped emotional energy to get on and do what has been planned.

For now, I want to emphasise that knowing these four Turning Points overcomes another core human problem apart from the kneejerk reaction. Mostly, as soon as the word 'loss' is mentioned, people tend to assume that whatever has slipped beyond our control is 'gone forever'. People commonly do not recognise how much potential capacity they have to influence situations in ways that empower them to recover just one important feature of life that has been lost. The *Prevent Loss* Turning Point comes with an attitude of *control*. If people believe they should be able to control life, and then feel that things are slipping beyond their control, they will experience a lot of angry and guilty feelings that may drive them on unreasonably. Chris and Peter were both getting these, and responding to them in different ways. Those ways are visible in the card patterns. Emotional Logic explains, however, how important it is to be able to let go of a 'controlling attitude' in order to move on to the Growth Cycle and learn how to *gain influence* in an assertive way, one that respects other people's values as much as your own.

The final point I would like to make is the way that Marian mentioned one of the potential traps that turns the adjustment process into an unhealthy reaction to loss. Peter's Anger and Depression cards were touching each other. This is a sign that, in his heart and mind and in his emotional chemistry, these two *'preparations for change'* might complicate each other and not fulfil their useful purposes. The Anger that could be used to prevent the loss of *something valued* turns around instead, to try to prevent *feelings of emptiness and powerlessness*. This drives people outwards to *do* something, *anything* that would show a display of power. This display tends to be destructive, and may seem to others to be completely irrational. We have found over the years in hundreds if not thousands of people that the types of behavioural reaction that result from interference between pairs of loss emotions is predictable from the two emotional *preparations* that get entangled.

To get an idea about how this works, you might take another look at the Turning Points diagram. Two rows of emotional Stepping Stones are shown. Denial, Anger and Bargaining along the top row are where people's emotional energy is preparing them with an urge to go out into the world to change things there. Shock, Guilt and Depression along the lower row are where people's emotional energy urges them to take a step back from the momentum of life in a busy world, and to reflect instead about their capacities to do things differently. It is very difficult, if not impossible, to do an internally and an externally directed preparation at the same time, such as Anger (out) and Depression (in). Try acting it out! These 'whirlpools of loss emotions' mostly resolve spontaneously when people understand how the unpleasant emotions fit constructively into a healthy adjustment process.

I explained in the Introduction that there is an important difference between physical emotions and feelings of emotion. The medical view is that physical emotions can start in social settings *before* the higher brain connects them into an awareness. The brain adds memories to the social experience to create a *feeling of emotion* that has a uniquely historical meaning and significance for the individual. Physical emotions are inbuilt genetically into survival mechanisms. They include social messaging (facial expressions, tone of voice, body language, pheromone chemicals in the sweat) that are common to all humanity – and to other mammals also. In this way, living creatures can anticipate each other's behaviour, which helps to build social groups for improved survival. Whirlpools of loss emotions start with people's feelings of emotion, however, and their unhelpful historical beliefs about those unique feelings. They then spread out to affect behaviour, relationships, and even stress-related physical and mental health. But all this is reversible by understanding your inbuilt Emotional Logic for healthy adjustments.

Chapter 3

Jess aged 8 turns her Anger to good use

Marian tells the story

Mrs Baxter made an appointment in morning surgery for her 8-year-old daughter, Jess, but came alone. She explained that she didn't want to take Jess out of school and, anyway, it would have been difficult to talk openly with her present. The problem was 'anger issues'. Jess had been an 'easy' baby and manageable as a toddler, but in the past three years her behaviour had become increasingly difficult. Mrs Baxter felt that a referral to Child and Adolescent Mental Health Services was now indicated because, as she said, 'I am at my wits end. I have tried everything, being gentle, ignoring the behaviour and, especially recently, yelling at her and sending her to her room. We don't seem to have any sort of a relationship, apart from always being at war with each other. Do you think she is autistic, doctor? Is that why her behaviour has changed, and is so unbelievable?'

Exploring the history, I gathered that Jess was an only child and Father had left the home when she was 3 years old. He now had a new family, but Jess stayed with them every other weekend and seemed to enjoy that. Mrs Baxter and her ex-husband had a 'mature' attitude, she told me, and Jess was not party to any conflict, 'So I don't think that is relevant to this issue,' she said.

Jess and her mum had a trip to London planned for half term. It was an early birthday treat for Jess, who was really keen on science and nature, and it was to involve a surprise visit to the Natural History Museum. At this point, Mrs Baxter, who had been showing excitement, suddenly looked very downcast. 'That was what last weekend's tantrum was about. I would have thought Jess would have been pleased to talk about it, but something sent her into one of her rages. She wrecked the Playmobil scene she had been making and almost broke the door slamming it shut when I tried to talk to her.'

I explained to Mrs Baxter that Anger is a grief emotion. Therefore, it suggested Jess was trying to *prevent* the loss of something that was important to her. Understanding her Anger could provide useful information about Jess's values. I passed Mrs Baxter the Life Cycle diagram and used it to illustrate that losses occur all the time in life, not only bereavement. However, sometimes, instead of moving us on to adjust to losses grief's unpleasant emotions can make us feel stuck if they are not understood. I then passed her the Turning Points diagram to point out where Anger comes in the process of adjusting to losses. She looked very thoughtful at this and, pointing to the Guilt Stepping Stone said, 'This is more like me'.

The consultation time had gone so I gave Mrs Baxter the Turning Points diagram with a suggestion to read about the useful purposes of Anger and Guilt, and we agreed that I would see her and Jess together after school for a long appointment the following week.

At that appointment, Jess presented as a polite, intelligent girl and rapidly engaged with the Emotional Logic process. I asked both Mother and Daughter to lay Stepping Stones cards for a scenario of their choice - something recent and a bit of a disappointment. Jess immediately stated that she wanted to lay cards for the fact that Mum had not booked the flight to London. Mrs Baxter, looking embarrassed, then explained, 'It was going to be a special treat, and it's a long way to London from here, and flying was surprisingly cheaper than the train, so I had said we would fly up to London as the treat. But by the time I got to book the flight it had become much too expensive. We are going on the train, but Jess had set her mind on flying because it would be something completely new.'

Emotional Logic has another set of Stepping Stones cards using picture icons designed for children, although many adults like to use them as well. Using these picture cards, Jess laid Anger first and then laid the Shock card to the right of it, and on top. Mum just laid Guilt. Asked about a time sequence, Jess to my surprise, said 'It starts with Shock – I can't believe Mum did that! Then I go to Anger and that's where I stay.'

I taught both of them about Shock using the information on the backs of their respective Shock cards. I explained that shock feelings are an early warning sign that something important is going on. These feelings are telling us to find a safe

Figure 3.1 – Jess's Stepping Stones arrangement – a two-card pattern
with the rest of the cards unused

place where we can work out what to do. I had in my consulting room a set of the materials developed to teach children in schools, and I showed Jess the child-friendly introduction to the healthy adjustment process that is used in classes to help children process their shock feelings. It goes by the name of the ABCD steps – Aware, Breathe, Choose, Do (see Figure 3.2). Jess found this very interesting, and said, 'I sometimes just go straight to the Do – and then I do things I wish I hadn't.'

Asking about safe places to plan revealed that Mum is a safe place, but Jess couldn't think of any at school. We also explored the useful purposes of Anger and Guilt. I asked Jess if she sometimes felt confused. She agreed that 'Sometimes everything looks blurred, and I need to do something, but I don't know what' – a beautiful description of the effects of a Shock-Anger confusion whirlpool.

We moved on to talk about Bargaining styles. Jess didn't recognise the words on the list, but Mum was able to tell a story of when they had 'teamed up' to rescue their cat who was stuck on a roof. Mrs Baxter, herself, ticked mostly in the passive list, so I took the opportunity to explain the advantages of assertive Bargaining over aggressive or passive ones.

While all this had been happening, I had a Loss Reaction Worksheet to hand for each of them. However, on this occasion I had not identified many hidden losses,

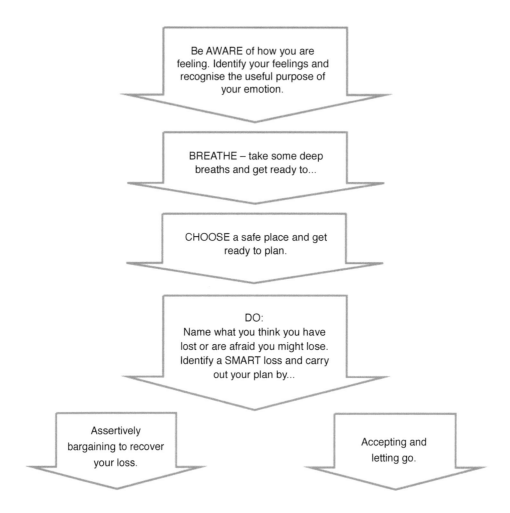

Figure 3.2 – The 'ABCD – Aware, Breathe, Choose, Do' acronym

which is unusual for me. Jess was still angry about the lost flight, and that prompted me to explore what had been so important about flying to London. She became tearful. She explained then that she had told all her classmates that she was going on a plane. They were all going to ask her after the half-term holiday what it was like!

We agreed together that some very important values were being threatened – the respect of her classmates, her telling the truth, being a VIP, something to talk about, being part of the group… Mum looked shocked, then ashamed. But then I could see that she had had an idea. She decided to take a risk, took a deep breath and said, 'Jess, it was going to be a surprise, but I think it would be good for you to know in advance. We are going to the Natural History Museum.' Jess's tears evaporated, and she broke into a grin, and gave her Mum a big hug.

Then she again became thoughtful. 'The girls in my class probably haven't even heard of the Natural History Museum. It won't seem as good as flying to them, but it's much better to me! Can we look online when we get home and plan what to see first? Will I be allowed to take photos?' Mrs Baxter, meanwhile, herself became thoughtful, then tentatively said, 'I have a box full of scrapbooking bits that I bought last year when I made that scrapbook for Auntie Anne about her big birthday celebration. If you like you can have them to make a holiday scrapbook.' There was a brief pause while Jess was obviously thinking, then she said, 'I know! I am going to make a scrapbook of photos and all sorts of bits from the trip. I can take that to school. That will be something to talk about. Maybe they will forget about the flying bit. Is that okay, Mum? Will you help me?' I just pointed to 'teaming up' on the assertive Bargaining list, and suggested we touch base by phone after the holiday.

It was two months later before we caught up with each other. I was told that all was going well. Jess had enjoyed returning to school and seemed to have made more stable friendships. Things were much better at home too. Mrs Baxter put this down to her insisting on 'a bit more of a routine, time to chat about the day, shared meals and that sort of thing. Just because it is chaotic when she visits Dad doesn't mean it has to be here too. I think she feels safer with some boundaries.'

I congratulated her, but decided against mentioning the move from passive to assertive parenting.

Trevor reflects on what happened here

This lovely story shows how managing a small incident in a new way can change years of history in a relationship. Small differences grow bigger over time when people's lives interact. Recognising small differences in grieving patterns early on, and then saying something helpfully responsive as soon as is reasonable, can save decades of trouble.

After five years of being a single mum, Mrs Baxter knew that something was going wrong. She thought she was handling the separation from her husband responsibly, but if so, why would her daughter's behaviour have deteriorated over the last three years? The society she lived in did not think in terms of grieving patterns affecting relationships over a medium or long term. It looked for a diagnosis and a cure of the individual now.

Fortunately, this doctor knew that grief affects relationships more commonly than autism, and even autism may in part be a pattern of grieving, so Marian was 'listening' for any signs of grieving in the story that she invited Mrs Baxter to share. Were any loss emotions expressed? Was something missing in life that one person in the relationship felt was important? Marian knew that Emotional Logic provides lots of helpful things to say in response to any identified losses, so she was not afraid to look into this.

Marian already had a hint about styles of grieving that differed between Jess and her mum. When Mrs Baxter had held the Turning Points diagram, she had pointed to the Guilt Stepping Stone saying, 'That is more like me'. Small differences? Jess was grieving differently.

And here we see the power of the emotional Stepping Stones cards to map these differences. Many people lay down several cards in unique patterns, but sometimes people put down only one, and that is that happened with Mrs Baxter. In relation to her 8-year-old daughter's behaviour, her single Guilt card showed the prevailing emotional atmosphere of the 'emotionally available adult' who was looking after Jess most of the time. That is what Jess was encountering at home at that deeper, subtle, heart-level, while her mother imagined that she had successfully protected Jess from any conflict in the background.

Jess, using the 'picture cards' as we call them, placed her obvious, up-front emotion first – Anger – and then placed a second emotion to the right and on top of it – Shock. She explained then why she was putting it there. The hidden story emerged *after* the emotion had been effectively communicated! I think that is an interesting point. What is it telling us?

Communicating the emotions effectively using the cards, and knowing that Mum had 'heard it', gave Jess the courage or permission to add the reason. The emotion first conveys a subtle message: 'This is important!' It could alert a responsive person to pay attention and cooperate to find a way forward. However, if people do not know that emotions are pre-verbal messages about *unnamed personal values*, they tend to see loud unpleasant emotion as mere bad behaviour that needs controlling. Activating their inner Emotional Logic, however, takes people beyond that to discovering the personal values that lie behind the behaviour. Behind every behaviour there is a story.

The icons on the picture cards are worth mentioning. They are not facial emoticons, and that is important, because many people on the autistic spectrum cannot read facial expressions well. All the icons have some sort of *movement* in them, because changes of body language convey much more emotion than many people realise. This is why many adults prefer the picture cards, and why we stopped calling them children's cards. They are for everyone. We simply offer people a choice.

Handling the cards adds another level of empowering insight also, about how people process their emotions. Emotional Logic coaches are trained to ask first if there is a time sequence shown in the pattern. Does it start somewhere and move on to something else, or is it a snapshot of the way it all feels at once? You cannot assume that a card pattern starts on the left and moves to the right. Jess laid out a pattern that started on the right and moved to the left! That probably means that when the Anger erupted into her loss-related behaviour, there was Shock mingled in with it.

Over the years, experience with card patterns has shown that if two loss emotions happen at the same time, which they commonly do, they may complicate each other and appear as something different – as distress, or tension, or confusion. The mixed up chemistry of a Shock-Anger whirlpool makes it difficult to think clearly. It sometimes makes people feel 'odd and out of it' in stressful situations. Jess had said, 'Sometimes everything looks blurred, and I need to do something, but I don't know what.' That says it: a Shock-Anger whirlpool in *anyone* could cause inner confusion. Then mixed messages to others put confusion into their minds and hearts also. That is why Mum came asking, 'What is wrong with my daughter?!'

Shock-Anger has a different impact to the Anger-Depression whirlpool that complicated Chris and Peter's story (page 25). Jess was probably getting progressively more shocked over the three years since starting at school. She couldn't think of any safe places at school, so was probably doubting her abilities to handle the situations she was facing there. Nevertheless, Jess did not want to share what her troubles there were. She had opportunities, but had chosen to struggle to manage it on her own. Did she struggle to get Mum's attention to help her? Perhaps Mum was distracted by managing background conflict and feeling guilty, and was not as emotionally available as Jess had hoped. Perhaps protecting Jess from conflict had made Mum seem too passive. We shall never know, and it doesn't matter once people learn the mutual responsiveness needed for truly assertive Bargaining.

Being emotionally distracted does not signify bad character. It is simply a fact of the demands of a busy life. Even so, having an Emotional Logic mental framework to recognise and harness a grieving heart, and to know a range of helpful responses to make, does prevent bad character habits from developing. Human nature is built to interact.

Chapter 4

Caring for the carer

Marian tells the story

Kate and Mark had been together for 15 years, and had settled into a pattern where Kate was the person who needed looking after and Mark looked after her. She had never worked, apart from an office junior job for a few months in her late teens. When I first met Kate as a new patient two years ago, she had been literally quaking with anxiety. Mark had explained that she was disabled due to diagnoses of global anxiety (being anxious all the time about everything), fibromyalgia (unexplained painful muscles and joints) and chronic fatigue syndrome. She was on a lot of medication, and it soon became apparent that one of her main fears was that she would not be allowed to continue all of these.

They had moved out of London to be near Kate's sister and because of the attractions of the rural environment, but the move had involved some extra losses, especially for Kate, one being her familiar healthcare environment. She was happy to be cared for by Mark, who also seemed happy with his role as carer, as long as he could escape to pursue his passion for outdoor activities. He especially loved white-water canoeing and climbing, and was an instructor in both of these sports.

In the first few months, Kate and I met regularly. She learned some Emotional Logic, which helped her to process the many traumatic events of her early life. She even began a planned reduction in her medication. But this story is not hers!

Mark, apart from accompanying Kate on the first two visits, did not consult a doctor. He was fit and well… until disaster struck. One Monday morning Kate was on my telephone list. In tearful panic, she explained that Mark had had a serious fall while climbing and was in hospital with a shattered pelvis.

Over the next few weeks, as one of her safe places, I had regular updates from Kate. Fortunately, in the preceding six months, she had found the confidence to restart driving, so she was able to visit Mark in hospital. His recovery was complicated by blood clots and reactions to medications, even to the point that admission to ITU was discussed briefly. At last the time came when he was considered ready for discharge and, to my surprise, Kate was up for the challenge of caring for him at home.

With support from district nurses it all went very well at first. Kate slipped from 'cared for' role to 'carer' easily. Then she came to tell me that it was all becoming too difficult. Mark's emotional and mental health had started to crumble. She told me that he had, one morning the previous week, decided he could not bear the confinement any longer. He was going to load the canoe on the roof rack and head for the river. He had got as far as the front drive before the severe pain in his hips drove him to the ground. It took all Kate's strength, emotional as well as physical, to get him back indoors and into a chair. Since then he had been very low in mood, eating little, smoking a lot despite having given it up 10 years before, refusing medication despite being in pain and, in the past two days, saying that he might as well be dead, that if he could get there he would jump into the river. Life was not worth living like this.

Mark did not need a lot of persuading to see me for some Emotional Logic, perhaps because he had seen how it had helped Kate. I was shocked to see him when he came in with her. He walked painfully with elbow crutches. He had gained a lot of weight, but lost muscle bulk, and he looked desolate.

I went through the usual introduction, showing him the overview of the healthy adjustment process with the Life Cycle and Turning Points diagrams, and then asked him to think of something he had found disappointing in the last two weeks to put the cards out for. He chose 'Falling down outside'. His card pattern is shown in Figure 4.1.

We discussed his Shock and the fact that, by appearing in the middle of the time sequence of the pattern rather than at the beginning, the Shock chemistry would cause him to get his 'STOP' message while all the other unpleasant emotions were already on the go. This could feel very unpleasant. He agreed that he was feeling very stuck, and could see how late-onset Shock could contribute to that. He wasn't too sure about safe places, but on this occasion I wanted to move on and return to thinking about those later. We then discussed the *growth point* of Bargaining being at the beginning of the time sequence shown in his pattern. Mark said that his attempt to go canoeing

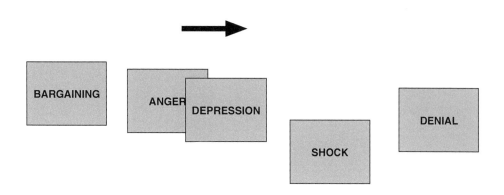

Figure 4.1 – Mark's Stepping Stones card pattern

was his Bargaining gambit to get back independence – but it had failed. Then, the Anger-Depression overlap was explored. Shaking his head ruefully, Mark agreed that the two emotions coincided, and when I showed Mark the whirlpool list (see page 165) he immediately said, 'Yes, I want to destroy everything, including myself. I can't go on like this. It's terrible.'

Mark became tearful at this point. Instead of risking him becoming shocked again by going further into his emotional reaction, I directed his attention onto the Loss Reaction Worksheet to see the root causes of his emotions. I had started to add my guessed losses to this while I had been hearing his story. Kate moved closer to him at this point, and he allowed her to put her hand on his arm, but it was tentatively done, and I wondered if their relationship had been under so much strain that any form of intimacy had been lost. I added this to the list for 'guess and check' when the time felt right.

The three of us working together rapidly found several hidden losses. Mark chose the headline loss: 'My Identity'.

Mark became much more animated as this process went on. Far from being weighed down by naming what he had lost, he seemed energised by the intellectual process.

Time was running out, so I did not ask him to do the tick patterns then (see page 11). I suggested he do them at home and that we meet in a week. Before they left, however, it was vital to find something that he could DO to recover one of the hidden losses. Bargaining styles had been looked at only briefly, but Mark could quickly see that 'trying to go canoeing' when he could only walk a few yards unaided was

LOSS REACTION WORKSHEET

Situation this worksheet relates to:...........'.My...Identity'.......................

1. Name as many losses as you can think of in the left hand column. For each loss try to name as many different hidden aspects that hurt which you can think of. Build up your loss reaction list over a period of time.

2. Then, think about each loss down your list in turn in one fairly quick session. Concentrate on each loss for no more than about 30 seconds. Try to name your feelings about 'that' loss 'now'. **Put a *pencilled* tick in the column (or columns) that has the closest fit to your feeling(s).** Carry on down the list of losses.

The scatter of ticks you obtain shows how much is going on inside you.

NAMED LOSSES	SHOCK	DENIAL	ANGER	GUILT	BARG'N	DEPR'N	ACCEPT
Dignity							
Comfort							
Going Outdoors							
Canoeing							
Intimacy with Kate							
Independence							
Instructing.							
Filling my time							
Enjoyment							
Adventure							
Caring for Kate							
Hope							
Being Useful							
Being Productive							
Contributing.							
My Earnings							

Figure 4.2 – Mark's Loss Reaction Worksheet

aggressive Bargaining. He turned the Denial card over now and said, 'I think I was using this – pretending that I was okay. Usually I'm good at assertive Bargaining, but with this wretched situation I have been forced to be passive. It's horrible not to feel useful. I feel so unproductive. My earnings from instructing were not great, but I am not contributing anything now.' 'Feeling useful', 'being productive', 'contributing', and 'my earnings' were added to the loss list.

It was Kate who came up with a SMART idea – an action plan to recover a small, achievable, relevant loss within a short time-frame. Excitedly, she turned from studying the list to facing Mark, and said, 'You can still use the computer, and there is nothing wrong with your number skills. You corrected me on my accounting only yesterday. Can't you do that online buying and selling that you once looked at. You have an eye for a bargain, oops pun! I am sure you would be good at it.' For the first time in that session, Mark looked Kate fully in the eyes, and there was a glimmer of hope appearing in his. 'Umm, maybe,' was all he said, but he put his hand over hers where it still rested on his arm.

A week later, Mark was moving less painfully, and he and Kate were joking about something in the waiting room when I called them in. The short version of the next session was that Mark had set up an online selling site and was talking animatedly about his plans, which unfortunately left me, the technophobe, way behind. I glanced at Kate, who grinned and shrugged her shoulders.

We revisited the Loss Reaction Worksheet. The ticks had not been done 'Oh sorry, I forgot. I have been so busy with this new venture.' Looking down the list, Mark looked surprised. 'Well, I seem to have got several of those things back. I have the possibility of contributing some income, something to fill my time, an interest that I enjoy, and I didn't notice that one about intimacy, but yes,' he said, 'our relationship is much better', as he reached for Kate's hand. 'And I know this will get better,' he said, slapping at his hip with the back of his other hand. 'I *will* be able to canoe and climb again, maybe next Summer.'

The prescription for antidepressants remained untyped – not needed after all.

Trevor reflects on what happened here

Marian says that this is not Kate's story, but Mark's. You may be getting the idea by now that emotions do not belong to one or the other, however. They are the evidence in each of us of what is happening in the rich networks of our relationships.

I would just like to point out that Kate was ill and on medication when she arrived, and it may have seemed that she was not a strong person, but Marian listened to her story, and discovered a history of childhood trauma, commonly now called 'Adverse Childhood Experiences' (ACEs for short). Emotional Logic is a trauma-responsive way of talking with people who carry hurts, and the evidence is here in this story that the growth of personal strength can follow trauma in time. Much of what Kate was experiencing was an accumulating effect of multiple hidden loss reactions over three decades.

Marian, I am sure, would have used much the same sort of conversational Emotional Logic method during those two years with Kate as she did with Mark, when he fell into his crisis. Rather than look at the emotional intensity of the big issue, which is so commonly the approach taken in therapies, Emotional Logic introduces a lifelong-learning method to understand generally how loss emotions can complicate recovery from physical, psychological and social problems. General principles can be learnt from looking at small situational examples. These same emotions, once understood differently, can then energise the *post-traumatic personal growth* of new capacities to explore life. However, when people are feeling shocked, they cannot learn or take the risks needed to get to their Growth Cycles. That is why the Emotional Logic method of managing post-traumatic memories is *not* to revisit the memories, as this will only repeatedly re-shock the person. The aim is not to acclimatise to shock feelings, as many therapies attempt to do. It is to equip the person to understand how to harness Shock, and all their other loss emotions, into a transformative and adaptable growth process.

All of that lies behind why Marian asked Mark to lay out a card pattern for 'something he had found disappointing in the last two weeks'. She wanted to start with something small, as a context in which to learn the healthy adjustment process to losses and the risk of further loss. By giving Mark the choice, it worked! Mark could make sense of what he was feeling when he fell down outside, by seeing his inner process slowed down outside himself in a card pattern.

We teach people to interpret the information in a loss card pattern by asking four questions, which Marian did here. By going through this standardised process, Mark could also piece together this jigsaw in his own mind. These four questions are:

1. Is there a time sequence to an adjustment process, starting somewhere and moving on in time, or is it a snapshot of how it all feels at once?

2. Where is the Shock card? It may be in an unhelpful place in the adjustment process, making someone feel *stuck* with unpleasant loss emotions. At the beginning of the process, however, its message to stop and find a safe place can be harnessed for helpful purposes.
3. Where are the Bargaining and Acceptance cards? These are the ways out of feeling stuck. They are the two active growth points, where people explore new possible action to move life forward. If these are not in the pattern, or are unhelpfully placed, or misunderstood, then people will be feeling *trapped* as well as stuck, which is worse.
4. Are there any overlaps? These may suggest whirlpools of loss emotions that can complicate the adjustment process. They steal energy for potential adjustment action, and they twist it into the experience of distress, tension or confusion. People can then feel *in turmoil*, as well as stuck and trapped.

Mark was stuck, trapped and in turmoil. Not a nice place to be!

In addition, Mark's overlapping cards were the ones we have come across before – Anger and Depression. Hearing what Mark said, Marian affirmed that these two 'physical preparation states for action or withdrawal from situations' were indeed complicating each other. He was in a destructive whirlpool of loss emotions.

Why did Marian not respond to his tears at that point by giving him an opportunity to talk about his feelings? Look at the sequence in the card pattern. What comes after the destructive whirlpool? Shock. Shock is 'doubting my resources to handle this'. *The last thing* we want to do to a traumatised person is to re-traumatise them by recovering memories.

One thing we have learnt from using loss emotion cards is that men are as emotionally literate as women when it comes to healthy adjustment to change. You can see it in the way they handle the cards. The difference is that women tend to be better at naming their feelings as emotions, while men tend to act on them straight away, but often without thinking. Emotional Logic aims to bring thinking and emotional energy into a reasoned partnership for *creative action in social settings*.

Knowing this about Emotional Logic, Marian moved rapidly onto the powerhouse for change – the Loss Reaction Worksheet – not allowing time for Mark to re-shock himself. It worked!

Having a sheet of paper 'out there' focused a collaborative exploration of personal values between Marian, Mark and Kate. The list of hidden losses is in fact a list of Mark's personal values. Truly it is his identity, written out for all to see. This enables an agreed single value to be the foundation for the next few days' continuing exploration – how to build a future that recovers or preserves *that* value, his capacity to contribute to the finances?

Mark had Bargained ineffectively to recover his independence. He reactivated his ability to Bargain effectively to recover something else – his capacity to contribute. Having been on his Depression Stepping Stone, he moved 'back to Bargaining'. We call the Depression Stepping Stone 'the place of decision', whether to go on to Acceptance to let go of, or back to Bargaining to recover, a specific named loss. Although people feel powerless when they go to their Depression of loss Stepping Stone, what grows there is their power of choice.

At the previous appointment, Mark didn't name, nor even recognise initially, that he had first recovered intimacy. After Kate had suggested the SMART action plan, his look at her, and that hand movement, said more than any words when he was lost for words. It just goes to show that, to be truly creative, life involves being mutually interdependent, and hearing each other. Who was the carer here?

Chapter 5

A fostered teenager stops self-harming

Marian tells the story

Louise (Lou) had an appointment in surgery booked by her foster mum, Geraldine, who was a longstanding patient. Sixteen-year-old Lou came alone, and seemed cross at being there. Her monosyllabic answers revealed that she had not wanted an appointment, but was 'made to come' because she was on regular medication. I knew that Geraldine, an experienced foster carer, was not prone to over-using medical services, so I was intrigued to discover that Lou was only taking a contraceptive and a moderate dose of an antidepressant. In addition, she had just received a month's prescription before moving here four days before, so why had Geraldine booked Lou in? There had to be an unvoiced concern.

I tried to chat to Lou about where she had moved from, how she was finding her new school, etc. After a while she did start to thaw a little, and told me that her previous foster placement had broken down. She was now in emergency foster care and due to move again in less than a month. The sense of distress was palpable.

After a while of mostly listening to Lou, I sensed that she was beginning to relax. Perhaps my non-judgmental curiosity and giving time had made her feel safe. I decided to take a risk and invite her back for a long Emotional Logic appointment. To explain what it would be about, I showed her the Life Cycle diagram while briefly explaining how grieving for important things lost can lead on to a growth process, coming through stronger. Lou referred to 'my therapist' at one point, which contributed to my opinion that Geraldine's agenda had been more than protocol.

The following week I again saw Lou alone. She was less taciturn, but seemed on edge. As usual, I asked her to think of a recent situation - 'Something a bit upsetting but not the end of the world' - and to lay out the orange Stepping Stones cards (see page 8) to show how her emotions had evolved. Lou rapidly put down Guilt, but then shuffled through the others and said, 'That's it! Guilt. It's my fault, again. I always mess things up.'

Resisting the urge to go into refuting and consoling mode, because I know Guilt has a useful purpose, I handed Lou the extra set of 28 small green 'feelings' cards and said 'What about those? Do any of those seem relevant? If so, put them around the orange one.'

Lou found many more feelings cards that she related to. The pattern she laid down is shown in Figure 5.1. She said she was unsure of the time sequence: 'It could go any way.'

I explained to Lou the difference between emotions (orange cards), which are common to everyone as they prepare you physically for some sort of change, and 'feelings of emotion' (green cards), which each individual experiences differently depending on their memories. She seemed to readily grasp this idea. It did not appear to be poor language skills that had prevented her from recognising and naming more emotions.

I then explained that each of the seven orange Stepping Stones cards had four green feelings cards associated with it. Because her pattern included lots of feelings, there was probably more physical emotion underlying it than she had initially recognised. The good thing about this was that it meant she probably had more energy available to adjust than she originally had shown. However, it was unrecognised as energy, and therefore could not be mobilised to fulfil its inbuilt useful purposes.

Together, we studied the 'Naming Feelings Sheet', which lists lots more feelings of emotion. She quickly picked up the way we grouped them to match the underlying adjustment emotions, and started to identify in her card pattern which emotions were represented there by the green cards she had used.

We were just starting to look at the useful purposes of her previously unrecognised emotions when Lou suddenly broke off and began to talk about the situation behind the pattern. She was feeling safe enough now I assumed, because her true emotions had been heard. She said she had had a 'massive row' with her previous foster father, and had made him so angry that he had shouted at her, something previously unknown in the two years she had been with that family. It was the way she had reacted afterwards

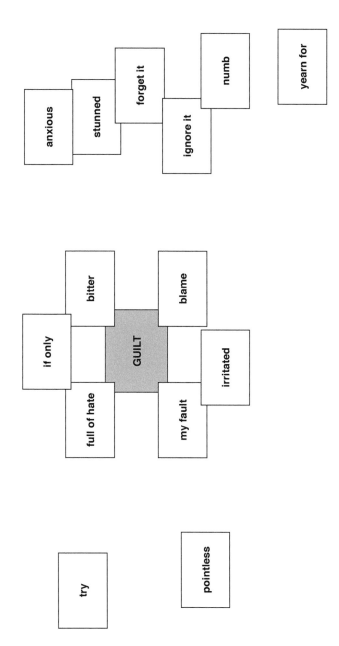

Figure 5.1 – Lou's Stepping Stones and Feeling cards pattern

that then had broken the relationship irretrievably in their eyes. They were worried about the effect that her behavioural reaction would have on their own 8-year-old daughter.

I was already making a loss list that included loss of relationships with that family, loss of a home of two years, and I made a note on the sheet also to ask what she had lost when unexpectedly shouted at – feeling safe or dignity, perhaps? Lou wanted to point out to me that 'full of hate' in the pattern was not for anyone in particular. It was for 'the system' that made her keep moving. 'Stability' and 'living in one place' were added to the loss list, as well as 'trusting the system' and 'respect for the system'.

Having heard more of the story, I thought it best to help Lou connect her feelings to healthy emotions, so returned to look again at her card pattern. She could see that anxious, stunned and numb were on the right of her pattern, three of the four Shock-related feelings. I always teach on Shock first. It can be so disabling if not recognised, and so liberating and self-affirming when it is. Asking Lou how her Shock felt, I got an unexpected answer. She said, 'My therapist says it's when I am happy, then low, then angry in rapid succession – I get confused all the time'. Hmm, I thought. That sounds more like a whirlpool to me.

We found the Shock Stepping Stone card, and I asked Lou to turn it over and read out the meaning and useful purpose of Shock written on the back. Safe places were in short supply. Many of them had been lost with her move, so 'safe places' was added to the loss list. I then pointed out that the Shock feelings were very mixed up with some others – 'forget it' and 'ignore it'. Lou identified these as Denial, and she looked at the back of this card, but just looked thoughtful.

The complex in the middle of the pattern was shouting to be analysed next. Three guilt feelings were correctly associated with the Guilt Stepping Stone card – 'my fault', 'if only' and 'blame' – but three others were unhelpfully there too. They could hinder a smooth adjustment process. Lou identified these as feelings that are associated with Anger, and looked surprised. 'That *is* strange. I *did* feel angry at myself for causing the argument. If that hadn't happened, I wouldn't have had to move!'

We looked at the backs of the Guilt and Anger cards, reading and discussing their useful purposes. I pointed out now that the 'ways out' that I had shown her previously, Bargaining and Acceptance, were also important. There was no evidence of Acceptance, but 'try' on the left and 'yearn for' on the right showed a glimpse of Bargaining. We needed to explore that more, later.

I now reached for my resources again and found an information sheet called

'Grieving about my grief'. It shows the seven most common whirlpools of emotion and the effects these may have on the way people behave and feel (shown in the Appendix, page 165). I explained to Lou that, when two emotions become entangled, neither of them can fulfil its useful purpose. The emotional energy builds up inside instead, giving rise to a behaviour or state of mind that is difficult to recognise as either of the constituent emotions. I asked if she recognised any of the behaviours or states on the sheet. Lou scanned down the sheet, hesitated in the middle and then she pointed to Shock-Denial. She said, 'I'm just like that – I doubt myself all the time, and I'm up and down – I must be difficult to live with.'

Looking wistful she said, 'Maybe that's why I've had four foster homes in six years.'

Lou had recognised her post-traumatic stress disorder from her early life. When things become too shocking, the memories may be put straight into Denial to avoid recalling them. This can make people very brittle. I wondered if this was the diagnosis that her therapist had made. Lou's eyes moved up the page again, and she began to look slightly shocked. I could see that she was studying the list of presentations of the Guilt-Anger whirlpool, the obvious one in the middle of her pattern.

'Do you recognise yourself in any of those?' I asked. Looking down, Lou admitted quietly then that, yes for several years she had been self-harming: 'Usually nothing serious, just little scratches with my nail scissors, and I always use Dettol to stop infection. This last time I went a bit deeper. There was a lot of blood… .'

Lou seemed surprised that I did not want to see the evidence of her self-harm. In fact, I showed little interest in the actual behaviour. Instead, I knew it was more important to explore the way out of the problem behaviour, by developing effective Bargaining skills or true Acceptance for some underlying losses. So I now moved on from this new insight to show her the Bargaining styles list (see Figure 5.3, page 60). I wanted to give her a sense of a way forward, having just helped her to understand her stuckness. She needed to know that it was possible to move on. So I asked her to go down the three columns ticking those she recognised she tended to do. Mostly, she was assertive, although she admitted that she had been aggressive in the argument with the previous foster father, and could be passive in scenarios where she felt unsure of herself – meeting new people, for example.

I shared my guessed Loss Reaction Worksheet with Lou then, saying, 'You only name something as a loss if it's something you value. So this is a list of your personal values.'

Named losses			Shock	Denial	Anger	Guilt	Barg'n	Depr'n	Accept
Prev foster family	✎	🗑	✔	✔	✔	✔			
Home of 2yr	✎	🗑	✔	✔	✔	✔		✔	
?? Being shouted at	✎	🗑	✔		✔	✔			
Stability	✎	🗑					✔		
Living in one place	✎	🗑	✔	✔					
Trusting the system	✎	🗑			✔				
Respect for the system	✎	🗑			✔				
Safe place	✎	🗑			✔			✔	
Prev foster mum	✎	🗑			✔	✔			
Little sister	✎	🗑	✔		✔	✔	✔	✔	
Trusting myself	✎	🗑				✔			

Figure 5.2 – Lou's Emotional Loss Worksheet

Lou had a light-bulb moment on seeing the connection between losses and her values. It was a more important insight even than seeing the roots in grieving that made sense of her self-harming behaviour. She agreed with all my guesses, and she became animated as she reeled off more things that she had lost, some going back to her early childhood. We filled two sheets and I called a halt. I asked Lou to go down the list quickly thinking, 'At this very moment, what emotion do I feel about that named loss?' and putting ticks in to indicate these.

Interestingly, there were fewer ticks in Shock and Denial than I had expected. They were mostly in Anger and Guilt, with a few in Depression too. I asked Lou to suggest a small loss from the list that she might stand a good chance of recovering quickly if she used an assertive Bargaining method. A loss with a lot of emotion across the row had been her relationship with her 'little sister' – the child in her previous foster family. I wondered aloud if there was any way they could keep in touch. Lou replied that she lived too far away to visit – but she had already bought a card with a pretty pony on it (the little girl was besotted with ponies) and was thinking about what she might write. We mused together on a form of words that would convey fondness and friendliness without mentioning regrets and explanations. I pointed out that she was already in the process of assertive Bargaining for this loss.

Lou had lost innumerable friends along the way with her frequent moves. She now looked hopeful as she remembered that in her next foster placement she would be returning to a school she had attended three years before. Maybe some of the friends she had then would still be around.

Lou left with her Loss Reaction Worksheets and with instructions to re-do the tick patterns in two weeks to see how they had moved. She also took a Turning Points diagram and a reminder note about sending the card. I suggested that she talk to Geraldine, who had been listed as a safe place, about what she had learned.

I did not see Lou again. She moved away as expected within the month. Geraldine said later that she had not self-harmed again while with her, and had talked openly about it to release the tension instead. We never came close to identifying what had been so disturbing in her life to set off so much early grieving that it came out as PTSD and her brittle behaviour. However, she took some new-found skills with her, and maybe when she later recalled the hard memories, she would now be able to grow stronger through it all.

Trevor reflects on what happened here

It is best for people to learn that there *is* a way out of the stuckness they feel *before* analysing the causes of the emotional overwhelm in too much depth. Emotional Logic creative conversations ideally explain *early on* about effective Bargaining to recover a named loss, rather than exploring feelings of being trapped in turmoil, tension or confusion, as a counselling approach might do. Clues to the hidden losses mentioned in someone's story can be noted when mapping the emotional world, but looking at the details and further emotional mapping can be revisited later. Marian therefore helped Lou to recognise her own abilities to Bargain and recover losses before showing her the Loss Reaction Worksheet that she had been quietly building up. So, when Lou suddenly had her light-bulb moment on seeing the loss list, she was already in a frame of mind to think that she was capable of doing something different about it, not just feeling overwhelmed again on seeing it.

This focus on Bargaining styles (aggressive, passive or assertive) to recover a previously hidden loss often surprises people, who may think that conversations with distressed people, to be empathic, should focus on the emotions. However, Emotional Logic's ability to engage safely with the emotional experience and see behind it which personal values are challenged is a deeper form of empathy. It potentially liberates people into an adjustment process.

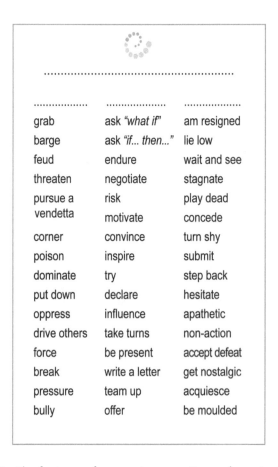

grab	ask *"what if"*	am resigned
barge	ask *"if... then..."*	lie low
feud	endure	wait and see
threaten	negotiate	stagnate
pursue a vendetta	risk	play dead
	motivate	concede
corner	convince	turn shy
poison	inspire	submit
dominate	try	step back
put down	declare	hesitate
oppress	influence	apathetic
drive others	take turns	non-action
force	be present	accept defeat
break	write a letter	get nostalgic
pressure	team up	acquiesce
bully	offer	be moulded

Figure 5.3 – The features of aggressive, assertive and passive Bargaining

It is a valuable reflective exercise to look through these three lists of Bargaining styles and make a pencilled note of which you tend to do generally in life. The outer two columns list aggressive and passive styles of trying to get back what you want. There are circumstances in life when it is necessary to be aggressive or passive to survive or get through the moment. However, if these methods become habits, they can cause trouble in relationships and ultimately lead to more instability and break-ups. On the other hand, assertive methods (in the middle) may take longer to recover what is important to you, but the solutions are more sustainable because they all build relationships along the way. This creates a more stable future in which those important personal values can be preserved. We never criticise people for using aggressive or passive methods, because these may be safe places for them given their past life circumstances. We always encourage people, however, to experiment with assertive methods to recover a single named loss or value. The more those methods are used, the more sustainable will be the resulting inner strength.

Some people call the first four emotional Stepping Stones of healthy adjustment a 'Stress Cycle' when *stuck* in them, to contrast this part of adjustment with the Growth Cycle of the final three. Rather than energising attempts to recognise or prevent losses, the feelings associated with Shock, Denial's brittleness, Anger and Guilty self-questioning can build up inside into stress and spoil life. To get to the Growth Cycle instead, it is a good idea to talk with someone trusted, showing them the Turning Points diagram or other resources shown in the Appendix.

With Lou, Marian had started that movement from Stress Cycle to Growth Cycle at their first short meeting. She did it by showing her the Life Cycle diagram, and pointing out its top right-hand corner. The preparation for this continued during Lou's long appointment, until that breakthrough moment occurred when she clarified that her turmoil of feelings concealed firm 'emotional Stepping Stones', which *help adjustments*. Lou must have felt *heard* at that point, and not criticised. She presumably felt safe enough to tell her story in greater depth, and out came the painful truth. She broke away from the learning exercise, having gained some self-respect as a grieving person. When that trust in a safe relationship is won, the honest truth can start its process of healing and regrowth.

Having mapped Lou's emotional landscape, it is the Loss Reaction Worksheet that provides the *powerhouse for change*. Marian always starts quietly making a 'hidden loss list' from the outset of an Emotional Logic appointment, which we all can learn to do in our heads when we face any new situation. 'That sounds bad, but what have

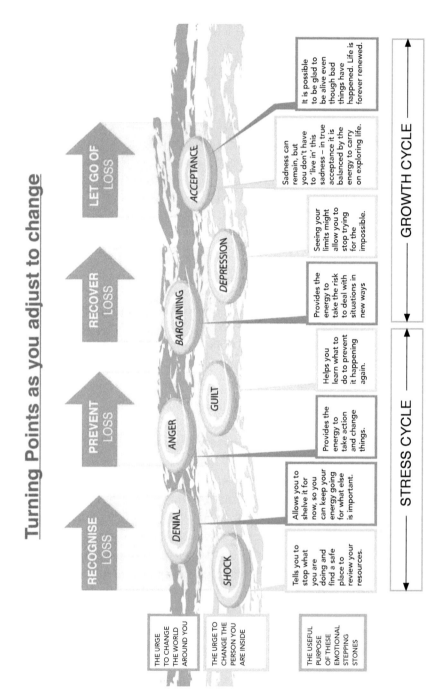

Figure 5.4 – Turning Points as you adjust to change

you lost, and what are you worried you might lose?' Every named loss is a potential seed for a solution-focused action plan that might enable order to grow around that named personal value.

The lights went on for Lou when she recognised that naming losses is one and the same thing as naming her personal values. She saw her true identity. Emotional energy then starts to re-align to fulfil its useful purposes. Tensions can unlock. Whirlpools or eddies in the flow of life can unwind. Decisions come more easily, and with them the emotional empowerment to see action plans through. By focusing on how to preserve the named value in its changing relational context, people also know how to respond to further setbacks more constructively.

Seeding potential order into inner turmoil occurs by seeing the Turning Points diagram as an icon holding steady within emotional turmoil. Another seed of order is to *choose* a small named loss that a SMART action plan (page 32) could quickly recover. Yet another seed of potential order is to reflect on the seven Naming Feelings lists that are shown in the Appendix (page 166-168). Each list of 16 potential named feelings in UK English is associated with one of the Emotional Stepping Stones. By recognising how our vague, passing feelings can be grouped into these firm *adjustment categories*, an inner transformation of our painful memories can start releasing prisoners from their pasts.

In different languages and cultures, local research can identify popularly used names of feelings of emotion. A focus group can agree which adjustment Stepping Stone they best relate to. There will always need to be some flexibility and disagreement about categories, but the capacity to talk more constructively about unpleasant emotions is liberating in itself. The healing is in the conversations.

The children's lists used in schools are also shown in the Appendix for comparison. Adaptive transformation of our inner emotional worlds starts when people are able to say to themselves in their heads, for example, 'When I feel sick in my stomach and self-critical, that is my Guilty self-questioning Stepping Stone appearing for me to stand on! It means I need to *prevent* something from happening again. This message from my guts does not mean things are all my fault. It means I should step back for a moment from this situation and learn something new.'

That thought process, based on learning to categorise our unpleasant feelings, brings emotional energy and rational action planning into healthy partnership. It does not deny the importance of our feelings. It sees them as *vital information about our values*. Rather than only trying to regulate or hide our feelings, we can use them to name our hidden values, and then build an action plan to preserve one of them. This helps people to be less self-absorbed, and more empowered to engage in an unpredictable world, cautiously, but assertively knowing that we have safe places to return to if things are not working out well. We say, 'You only grieve if you have loved. That makes you more of a human being, not less. Join the human race! The more you understand your ways of grieving, the less you will get stuck in life.'

We can only make guesses about the traumas that Lou might have experienced in her early life, which set her grieving going in unhelpful whirlpools. This is not the place to start talking about the range of Adverse Childhood Experiences (ACEs) that can accumulate their unresolved and unrecognised grieving. It is known that if a child grows up in an environment experiencing four or more ACEs (abuse, neglect, fear, inconsistency, for example), then their long-term health, their educational and social performance, their relational stability and even life expectancy will all suffer. However, there are three protective factors which can enable people to come through stronger:

1. Having one emotionally available adult (anyone – a teacher, for example) who is consistently accessible.
2. Being heard.
3. Not being made to feel ashamed of one's emotions.

The Emotional Logic learning materials can provide the consistency of feedback needed for new life to grow from within. The more adults or peer mentors who understand Emotional Logic and are emotionally available, the more our young people will be able to come through traumatising situations stronger. It may not need long counselling appointments. It may be enough to add bits of helpful information about emotions into everyday conversations.

We have examples from around the world of young people who have been able to stop self-harming after just one or two Emotional Logic learning sessions. This occurs when they realise that their Anger-Guilt whirlpool is a pattern of grieving for multiple un-named losses, which can undo itself as quickly as it started. The release from the pattern occurs when true personal values, kept hidden in their hearts, are truly heard.

Chapter 6

Preventing Harry's depression

Marian tells the story

Harry told me that he had come to learn Emotional Logic on the recommendation of an acquaintance, whom he described as 'a sensible sort of chap'. Apart from that, he was not very forthcoming, and he was looking quite glum.

As this was not much to go on, I decided to start by getting straight into some teaching and showed him the Life Cycle diagram first (Figure 0.1, page 4). I explained straight away, as I always do, that the 'Love' written in the middle referred to anything valued – 'what we love' - not just to romantic love, and I gave as examples a good job, or well-worked-on car. Harry's eyes widened at the mention of a job. Now he volunteered an explanation for why he had booked his appointment.

'I didn't lose my job; I gave it up – fool that I was!' After a short silence, he expanded on this: 'I am only 64, but that warehouse manager post was a bit tiring. I thought restful retirement sounded great, and they were offering a good package. The wife was concerned about money, but I was confident we would be okay, so I went for it. That was six months ago. What a stupid decision!'

Harry looked close to tears at this point. I guessed that it wouldn't be helpful for him just to display his feelings, or to ask him to talk about how he felt. I thought he needed to understand his emotions, to see where they came from. I drew his attention back to the Life Cycle diagram, and handed it to him to hold while I explained, 'When disappointment, setback or loss occurs, Shock sets in, and people often think, "I don't know how to cope with this!" Then a whole mixture of other unpleasant emotions may follow. They are there to *move us* to explore ways through, but they can get a bit overwhelming, and we may feel stuck there instead. However, this "loss reaction", as we call it, does lead on to a Growth Cycle, where we try some Bargaining and Acceptance to find a way forward. People tell themselves off for having these unpleasant emotions, but they are all there for a useful purpose.'

Harry looked close to tears again at this point. I handed him the orange Stepping Stones cards (see page 8) and asked him to think of a difficult, but not 'end of the world', situation that had occurred in the last few weeks and to put down the cards to show how he felt about it. I gave the instructions I always do about not having to use all the cards, and there being no 'right' or 'wrong'.

Harry, having looked carefully at all the cards, then firmly placed Depression on the table while saying, 'My wife wanted me to see the doctor and get some tablets for depression, but I have never been one for doctors or tablets – always very healthy, until now.' He then laid Guilt to the right, and then Acceptance, saying, 'I've just got to accept it. Nothing else I can do!'

Harry confirmed that the time sequence went left to right. He went on to say that the scenario he had in mind had been about a holiday. His wife had wanted to go to Thailand, but they realised it was beyond their means. An argument had followed, and his wife had told him 'to get himself sorted out – or else…'.

Showing Harry the Turning Points diagram to compare it with his pattern, I pointed out that Shock is commonly felt at the start of a loss reaction, and I suggested that he look at the back of the Shock card. It is always helpful for people to know where Shock fits in the adjustment process, and you never know what important things they might say as they discover it. Harry read out, 'To adjust: I need to recognise loss'. Then said loudly as an aside, 'Well, it felt as if I might lose my marriage!' He continued reading: 'It means: I am doubting my resources. Useful purpose: Stop what you are doing and find a safe place to review your resources.'

Harry stared hard at the words he had just read. He then put the Shock card down to the left of his Depression card, nodding as he did it. It felt like a good opportunity to explain about Emotional Logic safe places – not just hideaways, places to hide, but planning offices, places in which to make plans. I asked Harry what *his* safe places were. Harry thought for what seemed like a long time, and then shook his head sadly. 'I never realised work was a safe place until I left! I really miss the banter and the lunchtime chats.'

'So *now* we are getting closer to what lies behind his feelings,' I thought. During

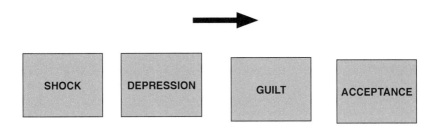

Figure 6.1 – Harry's Stepping Stones cards

the conversation so far, I had kept a Loss Reaction Worksheet beside me, and had been jotting down in the left-hand column the *hidden losses* that I guessed Harry might have been experiencing. So far these included: Job, Making the right decision, Finance, Restful retirement, Relationship with wife, Thai holiday and Self-esteem. I now added Banter with workmates, and Lunchtime chats. However, before sharing this list with Harry, I decided to teach something more about the Growth Cycle. It is important that people should know there is a way out of the problem *before* going into depth to describe the problem itself.

So next, as part of this guided learning strategy, I asked Harry to read the back of the Depression Stepping Stone card, which surprisingly is part of the Growth Cycle. He seemed almost afraid to pick it up at first, but then read: 'To adjust: I need to recover loss. It means: I feel empty and powerless'. Here he nodded slowly, then continued: 'Useful purpose: Recognising my limits might allow me to stop trying for the impossible.'

'I don't like having limits,' he stated bitterly.

Realising this was getting close to the big issue for Harry, I decided to move to that phase of an Emotional Logic 'creative conversation' where we start to look at solutions rather than only map where the emotional energy is trapped. That meant showing him the Growth Cycle roundabout diagram. I offered it to him to hold while I explained about the surprisingly healthy place of depressive feelings of emptiness or powerlessness as one important part of a loss reaction, a part that leads on to exploring new ways forward.

The Depression of loss is like a layby, or resting place, when we get tired of going around and around, trying and failing to recover a loss, and not feeling able to let go of it. Having found a safe place to name what we miss, we can learn about our limits, then explore our limits with increased wisdom.

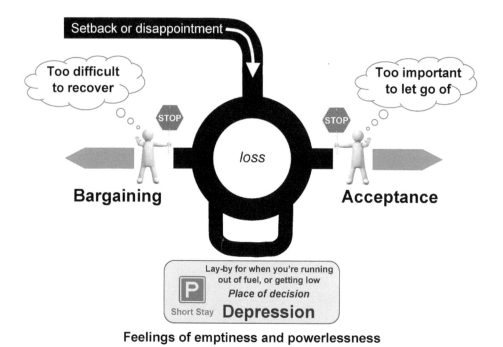

Figure 6.2 – The Growth Cycle roundabout diagram

Harry jumped on this one, saying rather angrily, 'I am certainly wiser *after* the event – but I can't see how that helps! It just makes me feel more Guilty for making such a wrong decision.' So, teaching on Guilt followed. Harry quickly understood the idea of it being about learning to prevent things happening again, and he even made the connection of the place of Anger alongside this. However, he pointed out that there wouldn't be a 'next time' for giving up a job of 30 years. 'Another chance' was quietly added to the growing list of hidden losses packed inside this situation.

I wanted to get back to the solution-focused phase of the Emotional Logic conversation, so I drew Harry's attention to the Bargaining card and asked him to turn it over, knowing that this would be the most vital area of new learning to activate his Growth Cycle. 'Bargaining is what you *do* to get back something that you value that has *actually gone*, so you can no longer prevent its loss. But there is still lots you can do, if you carefully name what it is you really want back. The feelings that move you to try some Bargaining are things like yearning, or longing, or wanting to fill the gap.' Harry nodded slowly. 'But there are different styles of Bargaining; and they have a huge impact on whether or not people succeed. Would you like to have a look at yours, Harry?'

Harry seemed livelier at this point, sitting forward as I put the 'Naming Feelings' sheet (see page 168) in front of him, with a pencil. As asked, he ringed the words on the three-column card about what he tended to do generally in life, not just in this situation, and an interesting turn of the conversation followed. Harry had lots of words ringed in the assertive and the passive styles columns, but only one in the aggressive style. He then said that he used to always use those assertive methods at work and at home, he thought, to move situations along, but in the last two months he now recognised he had been lying low, and stepping back, and even 'playing dead' by refusing to emerge from under the bedcovers the morning after the argument. That had triggered his wife's comment.

We discussed then how passive Bargaining could break relationships just as much as aggressive methods of Bargaining might. Harry looked a little embarrassed at this point, and then he said, 'I guess she has had losses too – that holiday she had planned for years, and having a grumpy old man under her feet all day – it can't be easy!'

I had one of *my* lightbulb moments. His mention of the word 'losses' in that way meant for me that a major shift had occurred in his thinking. We aim to help people to retell the story of a situation using the language of loss constructively. Now I could show him the Loss Reaction Worksheet I had been making my guesses on. 'It is not just the job that is driving your mood and upsetting your wife,' I said. 'You've had a major life change, and all the losses hidden behind that are building up. Have a look at this,' I said, and gave him the worksheet. 'Each one of those hidden losses is starting its own grief reaction, one adding on top of another.'

I asked him to check it to see if he agreed that the losses listed were all *his* values, and not just my ideas. He said that the Thai holiday was his wife's dream, but he was sure there would be mosquitos and he wouldn't like the food. He could easily let that one go. I rubbed it out (which is why I use a pencil to write my guesses). Harry astutely noticed that I had duplicated 'making the right decision', and wanted to replace one of them with 'being a good husband'.

Having agreed that this was a list of Harry's personal values in this situation, I asked him next to tick the emotions that he felt 'right now' about each of the losses we had listed. He asked to look at the backs of the remaining cards, and he noted that his

Loss Reaction Worksheet

❷ View instructions   ⟶ Exit

✓ Saved

Title

Harry's unhappy retirement

Description

Wife said 'Get yourself sorted"

Named losses		Shock	Denial	Anger	Guilt	Barg'n	Depr'n	Accept
Job	✎ 🗑	✓		✓	✓		✓	
Making the right decision	✎ 🗑				✓		✓	
Finance	✎ 🗑	✓		✓	✓		✓	
Restful retirement	✎ 🗑						✓	
Relationship with wife	✎ 🗑	✓			✓	✓	✓	
My good health	✎ 🗑					✓		✓
Self esteem	✎ 🗑						✓	
Safe places - work	✎ 🗑			✓			✓	
Safe places - wife	✎ 🗑	✓			✓		✓	
Banter	✎ 🗑					✓		
Lunchtime chats	✎ 🗑			✓		✓		
Being limitless	✎ 🗑	✓			✓		✓	
Another chance	✎ 🗑						✓	✓
Being a good husband	✎ 🗑	✓			✓	✓	✓	
Name a loss ➕								
Totals		6	0	4	7	5	11	2

Figure 6.3 – Harry's Loss Reaction Worksheet

'Acceptance' didn't really sound like 'life is forever renewed'. He began to helpfully question if maybe his feeling wasn't true Acceptance, in the Emotional Logic sense of being able to explore something new. 'Having no option but to accept it' is really part of depressive powerlessness, but as he began to map his many emotions onto the list of hidden losses that had built up over the months, he was beginning to see something new now.

Harry went down the list one by one, and his 'tick pattern' appeared as he went through it. Because the question is 'right now', even if a named loss occurred a long time ago, the tick pattern shows how someone's inner heart is tensioned at the very moment when a decision needs to be made about what is best to do to move on. Unrecognised, that tension or distress or confusion might produce an unhelpful style of Bargaining. On the other hand, displayed like this on the Worksheet it reveals the available energy to make a constructive move forward. Seeing the loss list on the left renews a person's *power of choice*. It empowers them to focus on just one of the named losses first, to see it as a personal value, and then to make an action plan that will establish that value in future developments.

Harry was surprised that his pattern showed so much Shock along with his Depression and his guilty feelings. He picked up the Shock card again and read its back. 'You know,' he said, 'I'm beginning to get an idea. It's the idea of safe places that has got me. There's no point in planning when you're feeling under pressure and stressed. That just leads to reacting to all the wrong things, and I turned passive and hid. I may not be at work, but it's still a safe place for me. And I'm thinking of Joe. I haven't seen him for ages, but we used to enjoy a bit of banter and a game of darts with a pint at lunchtime. Perhaps we could take that up again, but after work instead sometimes.'

'That sounds like a SMART idea,' I said. 'A small, achievable, relevant thing you can do in a short period of time to get back something important to you. And you'll certainly know when you've successfully done it, so you can congratulate yourself for it as well.'

'And another thing,' said Harry. 'He does a lot of travelling with his wife. He was away when I left, and I've somehow never caught up with him since. But, you know, he might have some good ideas about where Molly and I could go for a holiday.'

'That sounds even better,' I responded. 'It so often happens that when a bit of movement returns and we recover just one small loss, then we discover that others come back along with it, such as self-esteem, for example.'

For the first time, Harry smiled and looked properly at me. He leaned forward and took hold of his Loss Reaction Worksheet. I suddenly realised that he had been feeling really ashamed of himself, and now he wasn't. I remembered his Shock and his Guilt. If they had been tangling together into a whirlpool that might have generated the feelings of shame that his wife Molly had been calling depression.

While I was musing about this possibility, Harry had been avidly scanning down his Loss Reaction Worksheet. 'Hey, guess what!' he said, almost excitedly. 'If I call Joe, I can recover nearly everything on this list, except my job and maybe the finance. But I'll get another chance to get the holiday right and do the right thing by Molly. Who knows, the possibilities might be limitless!'

'That clinches it,' I thought. 'Such a rapid turnaround means he couldn't have been clinically depressed. He was full of regrets and shame – grieving, in fact.' Just as well he didn't end up on tablets.

Trevor reflects on what happened here

When you understand the useful purposes of your Shock feelings, as messages to get to a safe place to do some planning, you can quickly activate your inbuilt Emotional Logic and thus prevent *anxiety* from building up. Emotional Logic teaches a parallel process that prevents the Depression of loss from twisting around and building up into the illness called *clinical depression*. Marian demonstrated that process here with Harry.

To prevent anxiety, getting to a safe place is important (physical place, frame of mind, safe person), where you can congratulate yourself for recognising your Shock, rather than telling yourself off for having those feelings. Then you can start planning straight away, and you can emerge from your safe place with an action plan. As you connect with the unpredictable world, you will still know that if things do not turn out as you had planned you can get back to another safe place and start over again.

That 'getting back to a safe place' is what we mean by the 'Depression layby' on the Growth Cycle roundabout. It is a resting place in the adjustment process for planning and re-thinking, equivalent to safe places when feeling shocked. Nothing will make those horrible feelings of depressive emptiness and powerlessness pleasant, because we are not supposed to stay there, but rather than just driving ourselves on by using Denial, if we understand why these feelings are unpleasant, we can choose to temporarily make that resting place useful, with a creative adjustment purpose, before we pull onto the roundabout again.

Feelings of emptiness and powerlessness are NOT signs of illness or weakness. They are information about our values. Having seen our limits in depressive emptiness, we now can explore our limits in the lay-by and come out again with increased wisdom and having grown in the power of choice.

Many people present themselves to doctors and counselling psychologists saying they are depressed when in fact they are recurrently re-shocking themselves because of their ineffectiveness to get beyond their feelings. They are numb and stunned and unable to think. Harry was also ashamed of himself for making a bad decision, so his Shock was in a whirlpool with his guilty feelings. The illness of clinical depression may follow if the feelings of depressive emptiness and powerlessness *get pulled out of the Growth Cycle and disappear into a whirlpool with other loss emotions*. This removes the place of decision. People lose insight as well as everything else. The Growth Cycle is disabled, and the person is disempowered.

The relentless whirlpool chemistry of depressive emptiness with shock or guilt flattens off the body's healthy day-to-night circadian rhythm of steroid hormones. They are too low in the day, so people cannot respond to change, and too high at night, so people cannot sleep. This flattening *is* the illness of clinical depression. It takes time to develop, and time to heal. Whirlpool chemistry can be resisted, however, by understanding the rational purposes for the loss emotions, and by choosing to cooperate with them (rather than just get rid of them) to harness their information about personal values into making firm inner places of stability for reflection. I know that not all clinical depressions have this source, but I know also that these twists of healthy grieving can make any illness or vulnerability worse.

The Growth Cycle is genetically inbuilt as the way people explore how to grow stronger through managing setbacks and disappointments constructively. To make the place of decision effective, however, it needs to focus on the response to a single, specifically-named personal value that we have recognised as being lost, or is missing, or that never arrived. The decision is, 'Do I now take a risk to explore some new way to get this back (Bargaining), or do I let go of it and explore something else totally new in life (Acceptance)?' That is a different decision to those taken in the Shock safe place, but the principle is the same.

Sometimes there are no easy answers to that question. People may go round and round looking for options about what to do. Maybe one loss is too important to let go of, but there seems also to be no way to recover it. People start to feel empty and powerless over that loss, so pulling off into the layby to have a rest is a sensible thing to do. It can work creatively in conjunction with temporarily putting issues into Denial to get on with whatever else is important. The key feature is that *choice* is involved. By knowing where you are in the process, you remain an active agent. We may not always have choice over what we do, but we always have choice over how we do it.

However, simply knowing that there *is* a Growth Cycle in grieving enables people to transform this inner adaptive process. How does that work? First become mindful of emotional states and their useful purposes to adjust; then name some hidden losses that are driving all this emotion – ideally with a friend. Next, move from old, preferred Bargaining styles to try new assertive ones. Own your list of hidden losses as personal values instead, and then an action plan can result that recovers just one of those personal values.

Can you spot that process in the way Marian talked things through with Harry?

Chapter 7

Post-childbirth PTSD

Marian tells the story

Bernadette (Bernie), a 38-year-old Health and Safety Trainer, was referred for Emotional Logic (EL) by the practice nurse citing 'health anxiety' as the reason. Bernie had heard about EL from a friend and was happy to accept an appointment. Having checked it out for permission with Bernie, I had invited an apprentice EL coach called Rob to join us for a long appointment.

Bernie said that she really needed to do something about her anxiety as it was starting to affect the whole family, limiting their activities. The family consisted of her husband, James, a 13-year-old son, Arthur, and a 15-year-old daughter, Zoe. She explained the background. Her anxiety was making it difficult for her to travel. She hated driving on main roads, and chose the long way round on minor roads, meaning a longer time was needed to be sure of being on time. Her teenage children were complaining about this loss of time when she drove them to their various activities. Also, the whole family were becoming cross with her, because she could not face travelling far on holiday. Even the idea of taking the ferry to France filled her with horror.

The nurse had referred Bernie after a strange occurrence at a standard appointment when Bernie was receiving the normal result of a blood test. A GP had requested the tests to reassure Bernie, who had been getting excessively anxious about minor health issues, a behaviour sometimes called 'catastrophising'. The nurse had offered to check Bernie's blood pressure, as it had not been done for several years, and suddenly Bernie had become acutely anxious. She had refused, saying, 'I am so stressed, it is bound to be high'. The nurse had wisely responded with a brief explanation of how Emotional Logic might help with health anxieties. Bernie had agreed to a referral because, as she told Rob and myself when we met, she had noticed she had had a strange thought when the nurse suggested the blood pressure check. She said, 'It flashed through my mind, "My hospital bag isn't packed, and I won't be ready if it is high." I thought that was odd, so I decided to accept the nurse's suggestion of an appointment.'

Seeing our puzzled faces, Bernie explained: 'I've had anxiety ever since I was pregnant with Zoe. I went for a routine antenatal appointment, but my blood pressure was so high that the midwife sent me into hospital immediately. I was so afraid for my baby's life – and for mine too. She had looked very worried! They wouldn't let me go home until six days after the birth. I was in hospital for four weeks. It was awful!'

I thanked her for explaining, and acknowledged the depth of her emotion. However, as is usual in a personal learning appointment, I avoided following a counselling-type route of empathising any further with the expressed emotions. Instead, I kept to the lifelong-learning (that is, learning as an adult) belief that, on understanding an overview of the healthy adjustment process, someone could make rational sense of their own seemingly random emotions. So, on being prompted by me, Rob gave Bernie a copy of the Turning Points diagram to hold, and gave an overview of a loss reaction, from Shock and safe places through to a Growth Cycle. Rob then gave her a set of the emotional Stepping Stones cards, asked her to think of a small recent disappointment or setback, and said, 'Don't tell me how you feel about that situation. Use these cards to show me how you feel, either as a snapshot, or showing how you adjusted to it. There's no right or wrong. You don't need to use all the cards, only the ones that seem relevant to you. And lay them out as *you* understand them to mean.'

Bernie chose to place cards for a recent car journey when she had been forced to use an 'unpredictable' route. Rob next gave her a set of small green feelings cards (see opposite). These fill out the pattern to give much greater depth of insight into the movements of someone's inner emotional world.

Her loss card pattern is shown in Figure 7.1, with the arrows indicating a time sequence that she had demonstrated when asked.

With Bernie's permission, Rob and I spent a few minutes respectfully analysing her card pattern and being curious about what was happening for her emotionally. Rob had a small reprimand for being slow to start recording the hidden losses tumbling out in her story.

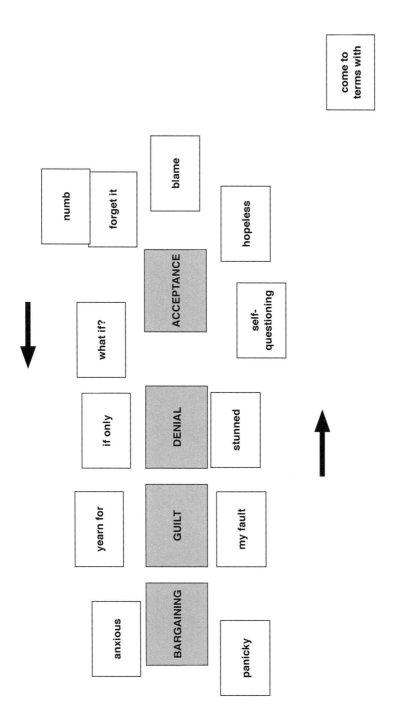

Figure 7.1 – Bernie's loss card pattern

The time sequence that she had indicated in the pattern was intriguing. Bernie had told us it moved left to right, but the 'come to terms with' in the bottom right corner was a future hope – not yet a reality. Asked what happened at the end after Acceptance, with that complex of feelings, Bernie said, 'Well, I go back to the beginning again! I go round and round.'

By following the standard four questions to analyse a card pattern (see page 50), we noted secondly that the Shock card was not in the pattern – strange because the presenting symptom was anxiety, which is a Shock-related feeling. However, all four of the green Shock-associated feelings cards were in – *anxious* and *panicky* slightly before Bargaining at the start, *stunned* in the middle of the pattern, and *numb* at the end. Shock was, in fact, spread through the whole pattern, but not recognised as such.

Thirdly, both Growth Points – Bargaining and Acceptance – were in the pattern, which might indicate that she did have a 'way of escape'. However, both seemed disabled by the surrounding feelings. Rob and I were making guesses that Bernie would probably be a passive Bargainer.

Finally, the fourth question about overlaps between cards led us to note that no orange cards were touching. However, potential whirlpools resulting from ineffective Bargaining were possibly shown by the placing of the feelings cards. We left this for later.

Rob started off by teaching Bernie about Shock and safe places. She was able to recognise that her anxiety was in fact her Shock state, and that this had a useful purpose as part of an adjustment process. However, she had difficulty naming any safe places. Relationships did not feel safe, as she felt ashamed of her inability to cope, and did not want to talk about it with colleagues or family. There was one friend who seemed to understand, who she might be able to share more with. In this scenario, in the car, Bernie had said, 'If there is a passenger, I just talk incessantly about anything to stop thinking. When I am on my own, I just keep talking to myself, telling myself *I can do this*, which sort of works but doesn't help the horrible tension inside.' I thought, 'That sounds like a Denial strategy'. And there, in the middle of her card pattern, was a Denial card.

Asking Bernie to look at the Bargaining styles list was interesting. Sure enough, she ticked many passive ones, but also surprisingly several assertive methods. Rob became curious about this, and she revealed to him that she was passive at home, but assertive in her professional role at work. The benefits of assertive Bargaining were already evident to her, which was good news for finding a solution-focused outcome later.

I now thought it best that we share our 'guessed loss lists' with Bernie – both mine and Rob's. As we went down the lists, she agreed with most of our guesses. Those she said were not relevant we crossed out. Included in the remaining list were losses that involved her family not understanding her anxiety, and practical things like 'getting Zoe to her piano lesson on time', 'Arthur being able to do two activities in one evening', and 'going on holiday'.

At this point, things went quiet. Bernie sat back with tears welling, and then explained that her panic had also stopped them flying, and even a camping holiday in the UK had seemed too 'risky'. She said, 'I used to enjoy adventure, but I can't do anything like that anymore.'

I had spotted something I wanted to share with her. I asked Rob what he would do next, and he correctly wanted to follow the active and compassionate strategy of choosing a SMART loss on which to focus an action plan. However, he suggested that we look at the adventure theme, and wondered if Bernie might try 'taking a risk' for a slightly more adventurous holiday than visiting relatives, which was what they had recently done instead of going abroad. Bernie looked a little panicky at this suggestion. Noting her Shock reaction, I chose to step in.

Partly alerted by my medical background, perhaps, I had noticed a hidden whirlpool. I said, 'Hold on, before we look at plans, can I take you back to something you said earlier, Bernie?' Distracting her from her shocking thought, I brought Bernie back to the episode when the practice nurse had asked to check her blood pressure. She had noticed her strange thought, 'My hospital bag isn't packed, and I won't be ready if my blood pressure is high'. Bernie relaxed on being given this opportunity. She admitted that she still had nightmares, about being alone in a hospital bed and afraid that she and her baby would die.

I was aware that childbirth-related post-traumatic stress disorder (PTSD) is increasingly being recognised as having a significant impact on mums and also dads. I showed Bernie the 'common whirlpools of emotion' information sheet (see page 165), and asked if she recognised any of the descriptions of the effects of whirlpools in herself. She initially focused on the shame whirlpool – Shock-Guilt. We looked again at her card pattern and noted how the feelings of those two emotions were indeed scattered throughout (Guilt is associated with 'my fault', 'if only', 'self-questioning' and 'blame'). With no *obvious* overlap, the whirlpooling consequence of *shame* feelings were nevertheless affecting Bernie, as she had said herself.

Continuing down the list, however, Bernie then pointed vigorously at the Shock-

Denial description – post-traumatic stress disorder. 'That's me! All of those things! Brittle – I burst into tears if someone raises their voice – but I thought it was just my hormones playing up. Stressed, anxious – well that's where we started. Fearful – yes, everything is scary! And I'm self-doubting too!' We all looked back at her card pattern. There we could see 'stunned' (Shock) almost touching Denial, and further along 'numb' (Shock again) was actually touching 'forget it' (Denial). Bernie's shocked 'freeze' reaction was being hidden inside her Denial.

I was able to explain that any experience where there is a perceived threat to life can be so shocking when recalled that it cannot be effectively processed, especially if safe places are not readily available. Then, the Shock chemistry gets pushed deeper into a cover-up Denial. Like a freezer, Denial keeps things hidden, but uses energy to do so. And when things come out again (such as when being offered a blood pressure check by a nurse), the denied feelings and memories emerge as fresh and raw as when they went in. In the postnatal period, everything is so new and chaotic, and the feel-good hormones are so active, that this type of PTSD may not emerge until much later when the initial trauma may seem insignificant.

Bernie was greatly relieved to know that there was a sensible reason for her 'craziness', but the suggestion that she share her new understanding with her husband, James, was surprising. 'I would probably cry, and I don't want to be seen to be upset again. I think he has had enough.' It was evident that he was not a safe place at this time. Safe places were added to Bernie's loss list. The SMART plan we all agreed was to assertively Bargain on building a safe place with her trusted friend, explaining to her what Bernie had learned. Bernie left firmly clutching the whirlpool sheet.

Over the next few weeks, I saw Bernie twice more. On the next occasion she told me that she and the children had had a water fight in the garden as the weather had been scorching. They had all enjoyed it, and James had been surprised on his return from work by the drying clothes and atmosphere of fun – a small step towards risky fun, perhaps, but a milestone. On the last appointment, Bernie had had to drive a neighbour to hospital using the 'scary' route. She only realised she had done it with *no anxiety* when Arthur had said, 'Wow, Mum, you wouldn't have been able to do that a few weeks ago!' The whole family were also planning a holiday – in a cottage on the coast. The teenagers were planning surfing and beach barbeques. Bernie said she would probably be on the beach with a good book, 'But that will be OK'.

Trevor reflects on what happened here

Bernie left that appointment 'firmly clutching the whirlpool sheet'. Here we see another example of kinaesthetic learning – of using our muscles and physical sensations to learn how to break old habits of behaviour and feeling. By keeping the *physical truth* at hand as she went home, Bernie could look again at it *out there* in her hands and learn to value her inner emotional messages, rather than be pushed further into anxiety by her memories of them. With that change of perspective, from memories into 'real-time relational emotions', her relationships were more likely to be life-renewing.

Learning the language of Emotional Logic also empowers a significant shift in conversational focus, from talking only about feelings and behaviours to talking instead about named personal values and action plans based on them. That is a subtle but important development. It shifts the focus from an individual's experience of life to a social activity setting in which personal identity is spoken out as 'what is important to me', and made real in agreed action plans with others. Self-respect increases when people connect with their values. And with that may come greater security to adapt behaviour socially with less anxiety.

During this 90-minute appointment, Marian kept the card pattern out on the table to refer back to. An immeasurable amount of potential information is revealed there, to be revisited time and again. That pattern needs respecting as much as the person who laid it out. I have seen someone move a hand to touch someone's card pattern, and seen the hand vigorously swiped away at the wrist by the person who had laid it, to prevent the feeling of intrusion that had been induced.

The emotion and feelings cards are moved about by someone intuitively until it 'feels just right' as a pattern. Those *movements* are revealing the hidden dynamics that tension this person's inner emotional heart, where their true identity of values resides. Those inner processes of preparing to respond have been 'photographed' in the card pattern, much like an X-ray or scan is for the body.

Many people these days have heard of 'the limbic brain', deep in the core of the brain. Here, emotions and memories are coordinated with the feedback from social and environmental settings that people receive from their senses. It is from here, deep in the social part of the brain, that the body's hormone chemistry is coordinated, which prepares the person physically for action or withdrawal in social settings. Much of this happens 'pre-verbally', without the words or language used by the higher brain cortex to analyse details. Seeing the card *pattern* slows down all these processes enough to be able to understand the details of the dynamics underlying preparations to respond. That empowers better decisions.

The subtleties that can be noticed in the way people move and place emotion and feelings cards is often awe-inspiring. Adding the feelings cards enables compassionate insight to the uniqueness of every human being. I can confidently say that in 15 years of using these two sets of cards together I have *never* seen two identical patterns. Interpreting them is an art form and science that can be developed by anyone who is interested in people. There are certain generalities that are common to all humanity, deeper than race, culture and language. There is also an infinite spectrum of unique details, which people lay out rather like handling paints to create a picture of their inner world.

One example is shown in Figure 7.2. It was sent to me from an EL coach abroad, asking me to guess at an interpretation with no other details given. (We play these games sometimes!) What does this suggest to you in terms of its *dynamics*? I noted, from my experience, that there is a Shock-Denial PTSD whirlpool at the root, and that inside that Denial there is also Anger. Why hide the Anger? It could be one way to keep it separated from entangling with the Depression. Why might that be important, I asked myself?

An Anger-Depression whirlpool could induce destructive drives for revenge out of the grief, but also suicidal thoughts, all of which would evaporate if the whirlpools of loss emotions were dispersed by learning about a healthy adjustment process. Perhaps this person had found that containing their Anger removed some intrusive thoughts? And what did the corona of feelings look like in dynamic terms? It contained three hard, angry feelings (bitter, full of hate, wanting revenge) with shock and depressive feelings also. I made a guess. To me it looked like an explosion. I replied that I thought this was a pattern from a soldier who had been blown up in combat and seriously injured. Correct, I was told.

Marian and Rob made an analysis and interpretation of Bernie's loss card pattern. Marian, from her experience of looking at many was able to recognise a PTSD pattern in it, which matched the story Bernie had been telling. Empathic connection on seeing her pattern led to a compassionate action plan, which progressively liberated her to explore life again. That is an example of moving conversations from feelings and behaviours, to values and action plans.

Post-traumatic stress disorder (PTSD) was first recognised in military combat situations, and then gradually extended to other life-threatening circumstances where

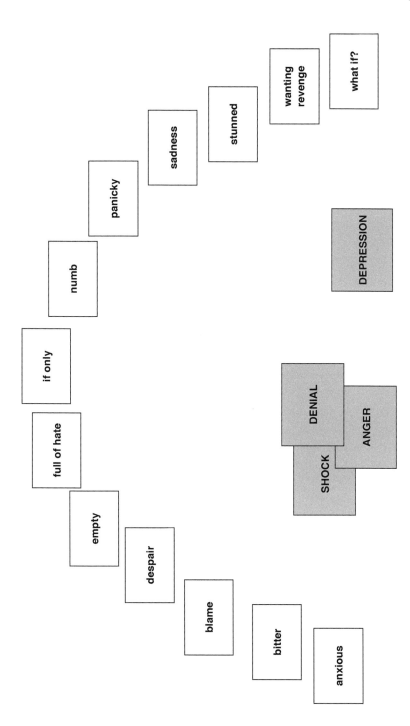

Figure 7.2 Loss card pattern that paints a picture

people realised they were completely disempowered to prevent loss. The emotional intensity is embedded in the memories of the situation. Recalling the events re-enacts the physical emotions, and likewise experiencing those emotions in other settings can re-activate the situational memories, making life so scary that no progress from shock feelings on to prevention strategies, or recovery, or letting go, can be considered. All emotion gets put into Denial. This is why Emotional Logic seems to oversimplify PTSD into a single whirlpool of emotion. In fact, hiding within that Denial state will be a chaos of emotions and feelings and scary behavioural drives. But the safe emotional mapping methods of Emotional Logic can slow down that recognition, and allow emotional feedback learning by looking instead at small, non-threatening situations. A renewal of personal identity can emerge that extends itself from managing small, everyday practical situations to managing the memories of bigger ones.

To manage and move on from PTSD, it is *not* necessary to revisit the traumatising incidents in therapy. This re-shocks people, and prevents learning. It *is* necessary to normalise grieving as a feature of everyday setbacks and disappointments, so that managing the day becomes less stressful.

In fact, there is a growing literature on post-traumatic *growth*. After adverse events, 30-70% of people come through stronger in some way, having learnt more about themselves and life. Activating people's Emotional Logic accelerates the pace of coming through stronger.

So, this is the wider context in which to understand the way that highly individualised, person-centred, Emotional Logic learning plans have a healing or therapeutic effect. This is more than psycho-education. It starts a truly lifelong-learning process of gradually developing inner strength.

Chapter 8

How to adapt and transform the workplace

Marian tells the story

Roger Tremaine came from Cornish sea-faring stock, but the sort of boats he had been working with for the almost 40 years of his working life were different. They were luxury yachts destined for wealthy owners worldwide. As Roger explained that Monday morning in the consulting room, 'I am an old-fashioned boat builder. I am not a computer button-pusher!' As the story unfolded, Roger's anger was thinly veiled.

His wife had made this appointment: 'She said I needed to get myself sorted out!' He had been sent home from work the previous Thursday for 'losing it'. As he told the story, the frustration was evident. 'I was supposed to be putting figures into the computer, but, yet again, I got mixed up and deleted the lot. When I asked a colleague, Pete, for help he was rude, saying I was too old for the job if I couldn't remember what he had told me before. And it was in front of the apprentice! I don't know what came over me, I just saw red. I squared up to him and I think I might even have hit him, but the boss came over and stood between us. Then, this is really shocking, I turned my fury onto the boss, Jim, who is a good chap, a friend actually, well, he was anyway... I told him where to go and that he could keep the job! Jim said I needed to come and see you about some "anger-management", and my wife thinks I need tablets for depression, so here I am!'

This morning I had not reckoned on full-scale Emotional Logic discussions, but this situation called for one. As a holding measure, I showed Roger the Life Cycle diagram (see page 4), explaining that when he 'lost it' he was already in a grief process, and a lot of other losses seemed to have followed. I reframed his Anger as a useful emotion when used appropriately.

When asked, Roger said he enjoyed reading. Yes, he was the sort of person who read the instructions before having a go at assembling something, so I handed him a Summary Sheet entitled 'Useful Purposes of Loss Emotions' that we use on our courses (see card wording in Chapter 2) and asked him to return in two hours at the end of the booked surgery.

When he re-entered the consulting room, Roger's anger had been replaced by a sense of powerlessness. He had read the summary, but said that remembering what he had done had 'messed up his thinking', so he could not concentrate. And now he felt that what Pete had said, about him being too old to learn new stuff, was right. 'Whoops!' I thought. 'I have given him too much information. I've put him into Shock, which got tied up with his Anger, meaning he couldn't think clearly. Now he is feeling that it is his fault (Guilt), as well as being empty and powerless (Depression).' I thought to myself, 'That sounds like the Guilt-Depression low self-esteem whirlpool shaping up'.

I decided that a solution-focused approach was going to be the quickest way to untangle these whirlpools for this practical man, and get Roger onto his Growth Cycle with some assertive Bargaining. So I handed him the three-column 'Naming Feelings' list (see page 168) to identify his preferred Bargaining styles. My suspicion, that he was usually a passive Bargainer but had slipped into aggressive mode when important values had been threatened, was borne out. There were lots of ticks in the passive column, a few in assertive, and only 'pressure' ticked in the aggressive column. He became Shocked again when realising how out of character his behaviour had been. I needed to show him that passive habits could damage relationships as much as aggressive ones. I emphasised the possibility that he could rebuild those relationships by focusing assertively on recovering just a single named loss.

Together, Roger and I completed a Loss Reaction Worksheet in only a few minutes. He was surprised to see how much was tied up in the incident. He felt relieved when I commented that this list, in fact, showed his values, and relationships on several levels were obviously very important to him. He commented that, although he had always taken pride in being a good craftsman, in recent years it was the people, especially the youngsters, that had become a more important part of his job.

I had asked Roger to tick which emotions he was feeling at this moment for each named loss. The resulting pattern is shown in Figure 8.1. I noticed that the Guilt and Depression columns had most ticks, which might suggest a whirlpool forming, but

LOSS REACTION WORKSHEET

Situation this worksheet relates to:...... **I told the boss where to go**

    1. Name as many losses as you can think of in the left hand column. For each loss try to name as many different hidden aspects that hurt which you can think of. Build up your loss reaction list over a period of time.

    2. Then, think about each loss down your list in turn in one fairly quick session. Concentrate on each loss for no more than about 30 seconds. Try to name your feelings about 'that' loss 'now'. **Put a *pencilled* tick in the column (or columns) that has the closest fit to your feeling(s).** Carry on down the list of losses.

The scatter of ticks you obtain shows how much is going on inside you.

NAMED LOSSSES	SHOCK	DENIAL	ANGER	GUILT	BARGAIN	DEPR'N	ACCEPT
My job – perhaps	✓		✓	✓			
Jim's respect				✓		✓	
Being capable						✓	
Being a useful team member	✓			✓		✓	
Respect of the apprentice	✓		✓	✓		✓	
Helping the youngsters			✓	✓		✓	
Wife's respect	✓						
Self-worth						✓	
Being a good role model				✓		✓	
	4	0	3	6	0	7	0

Photocopy this first, or make another as you expand your list over time.

Figure 8.1 – Roger's Loss Reaction Worksheet

because I was more interested in finding a practical Bargaining strategy for Roger, I also looked at the rows of ticks. Three or more in a row could suggest ineffective Bargaining to recover the named value of that row. Three rows in the middle of the sheet each had several ticks. This suggested to me that there was a lot tied up in these. Maybe his Bargaining had failed to recover something deeper about being a useful team member, being respected by the apprentice, and helping the youngsters. Roger looked at the list thoughtfully, and then said, 'It's just this computer thing! When it comes to the hands-on stuff I am in my element, and the youngsters really like me teaching them. If only we could go back to the old days!' Hum... There's the clue. 'That sounds like passive Bargaining,' I thought. 'That isn't going to happen.'

Then I remembered a tool called the Staceygram, or the Stacey Matrix, from the work of Ralph Stacey on how workforces adapt to change, or don't adapt. I quickly drew one on a sheet of scrap paper and explained it to Roger. To my surprise, he got it at once, and became quite excited.

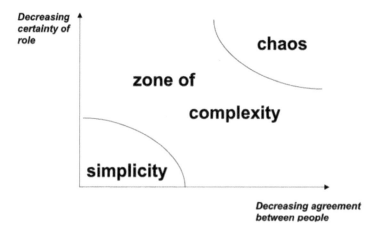

Figure 8.2 – The 'Staceygram'

'I see, of course,' he said, pointing to the top left corner. 'I don't know what my job is any more. And Pete especially thinks I can't cope with the computer, so he disagrees that I am in the right role. So that puts us up here, in chaos! It certainly feels like it. I understand about complexity, though. There's nothing simple about building boats! Every one turns out slightly different. I can cope with adapting as I go along when I am in my area of expertise, but computers don't play that game, do they? They force you to think straighter than the sea really is!'

I explained to Roger that moving from chaos to complexity involved temporary agreements between people where, for a specified short time, a different way of working is tried out and then reviewed and adapted.

By now I could see that Roger was no longer in his Guilt-Depression whirlpool. On the contrary, he was energised and making an assertive plan of his own. Asking if he could take my diagram, he announced that he wanted to show it to the boss, Jim, and see if a temporary agreement could be made. Perhaps, if he took a pay cut, he could avoid the computing. It would be better than losing the job altogether. 'I'm the wrong age to start all over again, and the family need my pay cheque.'

A little embarrassed by my rough sketch, I agreed that of course Roger could take it. And off he assertively went, but with a catch up appointment made for two weeks. Having seen Roger's Loss Reaction Worksheet tick pattern, I was concerned that if his Bargaining failed he might slip back into the whirlpools of emotion that I had seen, and head in a downward spiral towards clinical depression.

I needn't have worried. In a fortnight, a different, calmer but confident Roger entered the consulting room. He was carrying a well-worn Staceygram with his own annotations added. Showing me, Roger explained that he had demonstrated to Jim how his working environment had slipped into chaos. Jim was very interested in this way of picturing it. He had been keen to work with it as a tool to manage his growing number of staff as the business was getting busier. However, Jim had been surprised and disappointed that he was unaware that Roger was having difficulty with the computer. He had thought the flare-up had been a personality clash. He had been worried and upset, because he really valued Roger's input for the apprentices. Roger's outburst in front of that apprentice had deeply shocked Jim, and stopped him in his tracks. He had known that being a good role-model had been important to Roger, and news spreads, especially bad news like that, so something was going wrong. Roger then said that he had taken a deep breath and offered to apologise to Pete in the presence of the apprentices, if Jim would please consider giving him another chance.

It turned out that Roger's job had not been at risk from this one incident at all. His response in apologising had confirmed to Jim his opinion that Roger was the right person to be the named overall 'mentor' for the growing number of apprentices. Jim was clear that in that role Roger would be too busy to do the computer data inputting.

He would ask Pete to consider taking that on or delegating it in some other way, to release Roger into his strengths. Roger should concentrate on passing on his unique skills. There would have to be a bit of training – about how to be a good mentor – and Roger was actually looking forward to that. 'You see, I *can* learn new things if I am interested in them.'

Roger went on to tell me that he had decided some role-modelling and mentoring were a bit overdue also at home. His teenagers were 'riding rough-shod' over their mother, and it was high time they started to help out a bit. He had set up a family meeting at the end of the week, fish and chips and a proper discussion about sharing out the workload. His wife seemed to like his new style of Bargaining. They were planning a night away for their anniversary next month. He couldn't remember when they had last done that!

No antidepressants needed.

Trevor reflects on what happened here

This story isn't about depression, even though some people in it wondered if that was what was going on for Roger. It is about how emotional information about values can enter planning when change is affecting everyone involved in a situation at the same time. In that sense, it might be about preventing depression or any other stress-related illness but it's also about keeping people from going off sick, which disrupts work practice for those who have to stay on and cope.

It is worth reminding ourselves about the tipping point at which depressive feelings *might* escalate into a developing illness. This is relevant to how Emotional Logic works in partnership with the Staceygram to improve workplace adaptability and humanity. Roger's Loss Reaction Worksheet tick pattern (Figure 8.1) showed features of emotional turmoil that could have turned into clinical depression. A Guilt-Depression whirlpool could generate low self-regard and ruminating on problems or failures. Shock-Guilt could add shame and doubting his ability to do anything differently. Shock-Depression could produce fatigue and disengagement from life. But it didn't shape up that way.

Marian didn't spend time talking about the risk of depression, even though she could see the potential for it. She avoided the trap that psychology-based mental health promotion falls into, namely teaching people the early signs of a diagnosable illness, in the hope that early intervention might help. With Emotional Logic, spending that same amount of time learning the useful adjustment purposes of loss emotions could prevent that drift from even starting, and would equip people to handle future stresses more constructively.

So, giving Roger an Emotional Logic information sheet to handle while Marian talked him through it kept the learning about emotions in a kinaesthetic, visual, auditory… and relational mode. That matches the innate nature of emotional information about values all the way. The same information is also provided on the backs of the cards, the Turning Points diagram, and the Summary Sheet as text in text boxes, to address people's different learning styles (see the Appendix).

The breakthrough for Roger came when Marian set the whole adjustment process in its wider context of his relevant ongoing relationships at work. Emotional reactions are mostly the evidence of tensions that arise in relationships. We all have different patchworks of relationships, such as with the households we live in, local family and extended family, community and sports clubs, and so on. It is in the *dynamics* of those whole patches of relationships that personal values shape life. One mis-spoken word can affect many people at the same time, all in different ways, but likewise, one asserted personal value spoken compassionately can enrich the lives of many others.

Ralph Stacey's matrix, the Staceygram as we call it (Figure 8.2), draws attention to two clearly identifiable features of active relationships that can be talked about reasonably, even while they are actively generating emotions. The potential power of the Staceygram lies in getting as many people as possible in a changing environment to understand why emotions expressed during times of change are *not* part of the problem. They can be understood by teams as the evidence of people's unique values. When that is part of the everyday exchange between people, those loss emotions can become part of finding solutions.

As is well known in business settings, change management involves making temporary agreements to try a set of newly agreed roles, measuring the impact, then modifying the agreement at a review meeting, and so it goes on. There is a growing recognition in business settings that people's emotional states carry information that can be harnessed into improved performance and productivity. Some hierarchical organisations still use this to control and push people to their limits until a proportion crack into stress-related illnesses, but increasingly there is a view that organisations need to retain staff and evolve and adapt to rapidly changing business environments.

Emotional Logic can empower that shift from a 'wellness and illness' picture of make-or-break for staff, to an *inner strength* model of adaptability and transformation, which applies equally to individual staff and to the thriving of the whole organisation.

People need to be confident that honesty about their emotional responses will be interpreted in the 'healthy adjustment process' model of Emotional Logic. If so, the workplace can become another safe place where people feel truly heard, and can explore together their personal values and strengths in relation to developing the organisation.

Fortunately for Roger, his friend and manager Jim was someone who did take note of emotions as information, although he did not know how to interpret them or enquire constructively about them. Encouraging people to tell their stories of how they see situations is definitely helpful. However, by adding in to that an appreciation of the useful purposes of unpleasant emotions, groups of people could key rapidly into hidden values, as well as energise their solutions when the emotions evolve into a Growth Cycle.

In working with executives and managers, we have found that conversations may start on how the business is running and whether Emotional Logic could improve communications there, but they almost invariably move onto some personal relationship issues concerning family members. These are the stresses that leaders take to work and push into Denial until they get home. How much these personal worries surface at work to reduce performance probably matches the frequency with which work worries surface for the executive manager when at home, and reduce quality of life there. Any work with an organisation needs to be supported by private personal learning opportunities for the leaders. It is not wise to expose them in public learning situations where whatever is hidden in Denial might surface unhelpfully.

Roger spontaneously made that creative leap of transferring the wisdom of the Staceygram from his workplace roles to his home. Although the two axes in the Staceygram are named 'certainty of role' and 'agreement about role', in a home or social setting it isn't *all* about roles. There is also the question of belonging. 'Do I feel certain that I *belong* here?' 'Do others agree that I belong here?' 'What does belonging mean in terms of the choices I make in these settings with others?' To have honest conversations that name emotions and values around these deep questions can give people a growing sense of confidence, security and identity when they have been doubting, or telling themselves untrue stories based only on guesswork.

Roger had backed his work life into a corner by previous ineffective Bargaining. There are four causes of attempts to recover losses in changing situations proving ineffective:

1. You preferred to tell the story, or just 'displayed' it, without naming valued aspects of it that count as loss(es).
2. You have used aggressive or passive Bargaining styles as a learned habit.
3. You have not chosen a SMART loss (small, practical, achievable and relevant to recover within a short period of time).
4. You have tried doing one thing to recover two or more losses when each needs a different approach.

Roger's Bargaining had been ineffective on all four counts – but he learnt quickly. That discovery of effectiveness by talking within a wider context about what his values truly were was the tipping point that prevented the onset of clinical depression. To help people identify their SMART losses, we teach the 'SMART Question'. Let's say someone has lost confidence or self-respect, or some other intangible value. The SMART Question then is, 'As a result of losing confidence and self-respect, what can I no longer *do* that I used to be able to *do*?' This question keys people into recovering practical features of life, which gives them opportunities to practise some new assertive Bargaining methods, and that brings inner strength, wellbeing and adaptable transformation of life within reach.

The three phases of an Emotional Logic creative conversation, therefore, are (1) make sense of your feelings of emotion, but then (2) go deeper to name the values that are driving them, and then (3) make an action plan to recover just one using an assertive Bargaining method (see Figure 8.3). With Roger, Marian went through all those. However, Emotional Logic is not a specialist thing to do. Emotional Logic conversations can take place anywhere, anytime, when people understand an overview of the healthy adjustment process.

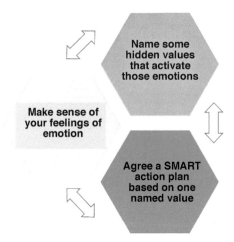

Figure 8.3 – The three phases of an Emotional Logic creative conversation

Chapter 9

Three generations read
Shelly and Friends

Marian tells the story

When 9-year-old Suzie appeared on my consulting list, I thought that I had not seen her for a few years, and I looked back at the computer records. Yes, two years had passed since I had referred her for assessment for possible autism. The follow-up letter from the paediatrician confirmed 'Mild high-functioning autism', but stated that Suzie was coping well in her small village primary school with half-time teaching assistant support.

Suzie's mum, Bernice, presented the current problem while Suzie looked sulky and cross, understandable when being talked about. 'She goes off on one for the slightest thing and can't be stopped,' said Bernice. An example was given of Suzie, on being asked to finish her tea before going out to play with the friend who had called, pushing the remaining food off her plate onto the table, kicking the chair over and screaming that it was not fair, before rushing for the door. On being intercepted by Bernice she pushed and kicked violently and refused to be calmed. 'What did the friend do?' I asked. Suzie tearfully joined in here, 'She left! It is always happening. All my friends have left, and it's Mum's fault!' Bernice threw her hands and eyes heavenward in despair at this.

I thought, 'There are more than a few loss emotions here – and several losses already mentioned or implied. I think a longer appointment is needed.'

A few days later, Suzie was more composed and was happy to show me how she had felt in this scenario by placing the picture cards (see Chapter 3) in her pattern. She laid Anger then Depression, but no other cards. She thought the Anger came first, but then said, 'I go back to being Angry again. I still feel angry now, even though I know I can't change it'.

Figure 9.1 – Suzie's picture card pattern

Bernice had also been handling some Stepping Stone cards for this scenario. She had laid Shock and Anger touching each other, then Bargaining, then Guilt and Depression partially overlying each other, as shown in Figure 9.2.

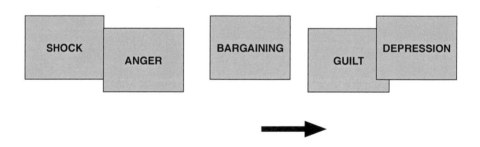

Figure 9.2 – Bernice's Stepping Stones card pattern

'Interesting,' I thought. 'Three whirlpools here, one for Suzie – a destructive one – and two for Bernice – confusion (Shock-Anger) and low self-esteem (Guilt-Depression). I did not want to re-shock Bernice by discussing hers in front of Suzie, but both of them readily recognised Suzie's destructive one when I explained it, and they both seemed relieved that an explanation for her 'over the top' reaction was available.

Using the more child-friendly language that appears on the backs of the picture cards, I taught them both the meanings and useful purposes of all the Stepping Stones. However, a point came where Suzie's concentration was visibly waning. She had been able to recognise both passive and aggressive methods in her 'Bargaining to get back what you've lost', which was a real gain. She had also perked up at the idea that Anger 'makes you heard', and commented, 'No-one listens to me if I don't lose my temper – then everyone hears!' Even Suzie was able to acknowledge then that her way of getting heard could be considered aggressive Bargaining, and might cause difficulties for others. She looked sad when saying that the friend, Ellie, who had called that day had been avoiding her since. 'Ellie thinks I'm a bad person now.'

We needed a SMART action plan to round off the session. How could Suzie learn to use her Anger without becoming aggressive? My eye caught sight of the *Shelly and Friends* books on my bookshelf. These are a set of seven illustrated story books, one for each emotional Stepping Stone. Seven Savannah animal characters interact as friends to explain the useful purposes of the unpleasant loss emotions as they solve everyday problems. I reached for the third book in the series entitled *Reggie gets Angry*, about a rhino who turns his anger around to help the Savannah friends through a difficult spot, and I put it in front of Suzie. She smiled broadly, and started to turn the pages. 'Do I look like that, Mum, when I snort and kick? I bet I do!' Bernice, unfortunately, was quick to interject that Suzie's reading capacity was below average. I was, however, able to turn the tables on this comment by saying that I thought both she and Suzie could learn from this story, so why not borrow it and read it together at home? I turned to the inside back cover and pointed to the discussion questions and the creative activity ideas at the end of the book too. Then I wondered aloud if, at some point, Suzie might be able to share Reggie's story and the related activities with Ellie.

Bernice responded that, yes, she had thought of chatting to Ellie's mum about trying to arrange a playdate. Maybe she would do that. Suzie still looked sceptical, but she went off clutching *Reggie gets Angry* with a promise to return the book when we next met. 'There are six more up there if you like it,' I said.

The next meeting did not happen for a few weeks, mostly due to Bernice's work commitments. When Suzie came again it was with her maternal Grandmother. 'Nan' handed back the well-thumbed Reggie book with thanks, but she reported that, although the Summer holiday had gone well, and she had been around a fair bit to help Bernice, the return to school had been very difficult. On the day before this appointment, Suzie had refused to get out of bed to go to school. There had been a row at home, and everyone had been very upset. Suzie, meanwhile, was looking blank and pinging her wristband repeatedly.

Nan and Suzie both laid card patterns. Nan's was for an unspecified event, and Suzie wanted to lay them for an event at school on which she did not elaborate.

This time Suzie laid Anger, Guilt, Depression and Shock very close together, Acceptance and finally Bargaining (see Figure 9.3). I was encouraged that she seemed to connect with the Stepping Stones cards, and they seemed to make sense to her even at her young age.

Figure 9.3 – Suzie's picture card pattern at the second appointment

Time moved left to right, she pointed, when I asked if it started somewhere and went on to others later. I noted that Shock came late in the time-sequence, which could be a bit of a problem. I decided, however, to ask what sort of Bargaining she had been doing.

The story emerged that she was very unhappy in her new class. She had a new teacher of whom she said: 'He is very shouty'. Her previous teaching support had gone on maternity leave and had not been replaced, and one of her good friends,

Rachel, had moved away during the Summer. 'She didn't even say goodbye!' Nan looked quite shocked herself when she heard this catalogue of losses.

Rather than look deeply at Nan's card pattern, I decided to move on and give both Suzie and Nan an overview of loss reactions and adjusting to change, using child-friendly language and a Turning Points diagram. I was talking briefly about the useful purposes of the emotional Stepping Stones, and when we reached Anger Suzie chipped in with, 'It makes you HEARD!'

That reminded me about the books. I had been thinking I should teach on the useful purpose of Shock and safe places by turning over the Shock picture card. So having turned it over, I then reached for *Shelly in Shock*, the first in the book series.

'Can we read it now?' asked Suzie, almost grabbing the book from my hands. 'How are you Bargaining?' I replied. Nan looked bemused, but Suzie grinned, handed me back the book and said, 'PLEEEASE'. 'That's assertive,' I said. 'Well done.' And so we did.

Figure 9.4 – Cover of *Shelly in Shock*

Suzie read most of the speech bubbles. I was reading the story out loud, about how Shelly the tortoise was stung on her nose by a bee, and hid in her shell for a long time as a safe place but did not know how to come out again. After a short while I looked at Nan, and asked her if she would like to continue. At first she was taken aback. This is not what usually happens when you see the doctor! But then she agreed and took the book, and Suzie, aged 9 and with mild autism, slipped across and sat on her lap. It took only five minutes, but that time was well spent. I could watch the interactions between them. Reactions had slowed down with the focus on emotions in the story. I wondered how much time Bernice was able to spend with her daughter, and what the argument had been about at home.

I knew I was running over time, but this seemed like an important moment not to lose. The final page, 'Things to Think About', could be turned to advantage now that she understood her Shock better. It had occurred to me that all the changes at school had robbed Suzie of several safe places. The three questions there were a good starting point to explore this with her:

1. Lisimba (the wise lion) said Shelly's shell was a safe place to have a really good think. Where would you go to have a really good think?
2. Who could you talk to, who could help you to make a plan to get life moving again?
3. What did Shelly also get back when she acted on her plan to get just one thing back?

Suzie was quick to pick up the theme about safe places, like Shelly's shell. She slipped off Nan's lap and flopped back on her chair looking sad. 'This class is too noisy. I just want to close my eyes, and cover my ears, and put my head on the desk and go to sleep. I don't want it!'

'Hmm,' I wondered. 'Does that fit with a Shock-Depression whirlpool? Or is it the sensory overload that many people on the autistic spectrum experience? Or is it a both-and situation?'

'At playtime I really miss my friend,' Suzie continued. 'I can play with others, but Rachel really seemed to understand that I don't like being crowded. And she didn't get upset when I needed to be by myself, either. We both loved fairies. I made a fairy garden and I really was looking forward to showing it to her. Now I never will!' Suzie's Nan reached out and caught her hand, as Suzie looked as if she might cry. She said, 'I know Rachel's mum. They have only moved into the city centre. It's not too far away.'

Aha! Perhaps here was a SMART loss that we could end this consultation with –

something Suzie could team up with Nan or her mum to recover. I wondered aloud if Suzie could write a note to Rachel, maybe even take a photo of her fairy garden? Would Nan be able to find an address, phone number or email for the family? Nan thought this could be possible but wondered what should be done about the school situation. Yes, despite any potential 'Butterfly Effect' from Suzie recovering an important friendship, I agreed that something needed to change at school. I suggested Nan talk to Bernice about contacting the school and explaining Suzie's probable sensory processing problems in a noisy environment. A quieter classroom might benefit everyone, but in the meanwhile, could she be seated in a quieter area? Perhaps a timely reminder of the need for a replacement teaching assistant would be useful too?

Nan looked hesitant, but decided then not to say something. Time was up. Suzie got up still holding *Shelly in Shock*. 'Can I take this home to read to Mum, please?' She had asked so politely that I could not refuse. 'Don't worry, I will make sure you get it back,' said Nan. 'Where can I buy a set? There is a birthday coming up, and I think we three generations can all do with reading these together!' And she winked, which was worth a thousand words.

Trevor reflects on what happened here

In years gone by it was little appreciated that most children and adults on the autistic spectrum had sensory overload. They simply cannot screen out sensory inputs in the way that 'neurotypical people' can. This leads to behavioural and relational problems, with high levels of anxiety and grief, with no way to explain what is going on. It is no wonder that many young people 'on the spectrum' become locked in and isolated.

We shall never know how much of what has been labelled as autistic behaviour is, in fact, an accumulating component of unrecognised grieving. The best way to find out is to actively prevent that grief from accumulating in the future. By helping children, teachers, specialists and whole families to recognise 'healthy grieving' at an early stage, all can learn how to respond most constructively with *emotionally-available relatedness*. Rather than having a dismissive, disapproving, or anything-goes attitude towards emotional displays, Emotional Logic provides some tools to reinforce an *emotionally responsive* way of relating.

In many places around the world, people on the spectrum have found that they can express their emotional world pre-verbally by handling the emotional Stepping Stone cards and then telling the story. It does not need a high level of reading ability. Many of these young people are highly intelligent in possibly a narrow range of capacities, so taking a 'strengths-based' approach to communication appropriate to each individual is key to emotional processing. Reinet Blignaut, a psychologist who runs a school for autistic children in South Africa, provided the original inspiration for the *Shelly and Friends* book series. Her now-adult son Joshua, who is at the high-functioning Asperger's syndrome end of the autistic spectrum of personalities, communicates best musically. A hotel in Pretoria has given Joshua permission to play their grand piano in the lounge whenever he wants to. His confident playing is a tremendous mood-setter.

The Shelly book series is an engaging addition to handling emotion cards. They help both neurotypical and autistic children (and many adults!) to get into their emotional worlds by story reading and storytelling, and then to share those inner worlds with others by sharing the story. Each book in the series is like an expansion of the brief text written on the backs of the seven emotional Stepping Stone cards. Inside the back covers, the discussion questions and 'express yourself creatively' ideas help people to discover new ways to communicate emotionally, and respect each other's differences. Figure 9.5 is an example of a relevant activity.

Although each of us experiences our emotions as if within ourselves, they are in fact the evidence of how our relationships move us.

Figure 9.5 – Emotional faces cupcakes

E-motion = energy in motion

Human imagination and memories can complicate that process. Mixed messages can be misunderstood. The insights gained from Emotional Logic tools can untangle those sometimes, which may add clarity to an otherwise turbulent social mix. The tools all slow down emotional communications and connect them into the personal values that make up our life stories. This all adds into an individual's developing sense of personal identity as a reasonable member of a social group or family. We are talking here about the 'systemic context' of emotions, which Emotional Logic enriches.

This context can go wrong, however. When other people behave in a way that we find disturbing, emotional energy within us can empower *shut-off and hide* reactions. It happens so easily in families and school classes and workplaces or social groups. When someone becomes emotionally unavailable to others, insight is required to prevent that from escalating into isolation and misunderstanding. Suzie's friend Rachel obviously had that sort of intuitive responsiveness and availability to prevent Suzie from becoming isolated. It can be learnt.

We are only guessing now, but Nan's hesitation to say anything in front of Suzie about the argument at home speaks volumes. Small differences between the older generations can grow into big problems for the younger ones. Catching them early has a powerfully preventive effect. In just the same way, small solutions put into place early can have a powerful 'Butterfly Effect' to enhance life. (A Butterfly Effect is a term from chaos theory that explains how big changes can follow from a small incident.) Many parents get isolated and overwhelmed at home, especially if single and trying to cope with work and family and home environments all at the same time. They can become emotionally unavailable even though they might love deeply underneath.

One of the tragedies of present-day society is that grandparents often are not available to help, or, at the opposite extreme, may try to take over responsibility, when empowering the parents would be more helpful for their grandchildren. There are often unresolved issues from previous decades between grandparents and the present day mums and dads. Memories complicate responsiveness in the now. Children often detect those tensions subtly. Likewise, they also detect improvements subtly. Imagine a spreading wave of influence if Nan and Bernice start to re-think *their* past history of unrecognised grieving. This might follow if each starts reading the Shelly series stories to Suzie. They then might start talking with each other around the questions at the end.

One final point I would like to make from this story comes from looking at Suzie's second card pattern (see Figure 9.3). Do you notice the gap between her Shock and her Bargaining cards? It looks small, but that is the sort of small thing that could also lead on to big problems later. To the left of that gap are her Anger, Guilt, Depression and Shock cards all touching each other. You will come across this pattern again in Chapter 11. We call them 'the Big Four'. Fortunately, Suzie is a quick learner, and Nan is a mediator in her relationships, so that pattern is less likely to build up over the following decades into a load of trouble. It will probably disperse into an energetic young woman with an assertive and somewhat unpredictable personality, who knows her own mind as she manages the boundaries of her need for quietness at times. Just at the moment, though, that Shock at the end of the string of emotions leads to no safe place. It leads to a gap. The gap is between the feeling Suzie, and the thinking Suzie. In that gap, this little girl is surrounded by swirling clouds of angry, guilty, empty and shocked feelings. Nan reached out to touch her hand – a small compassionate act that bridged that gap. It's the sort of thing that might have transformed her future.

Part 2

Emotional Logic in the community

Eighty per cent of people accessing mental health services are women. Eighty per cent of people in the criminal justice system are men. However you define gender, Emotional Logic's unique identification of 'whirlpools of loss emotions' shows how poor mental health and poor socialisation equally arise from unrecognised grieving. Emotional awareness using the Emotional Logic method illuminates a way to prevent recurrences of this range of problems by lifelong-learning about healthy adjustment to change.

Chapter 10

The street-gang leader
learns to Bargain

Trevor tells the story

Steve was a street-fighting gang leader. He had been in prison for GBH (grievous bodily harm), and had a reputation in the city for having floored a policeman with a single punch. He had been put on probation by the Magistrates Court after yet another incident. His social worker knew Emotional Logic and had suggested to the court that Steve's attendance for Emotional Logic 'personal learning appointments' might be made a condition of probation, rather than sending him for another spell in prison. This suggestion had been accepted, and thus he turned up in my consulting room.

I spent the 10 minutes of our first meeting getting to know him a bit, before deciding how to proceed. He spoke easily and seriously about his gang life with its sense of belonging, and became lively with a light in his eyes when he talked of the excitement of 'the fight'. He had been brought up in a violent household where you only survived if you 'got it in first'. When talking about his background, however, he lost his lively manner completely.

When prompted, he explained more of the circumstances of why he had accepted this condition of probation. Having been charged after another fight, and while waiting those weeks before the court proceedings, he had been in a bar drinking when, with no warning at all, a rival had swung a punch at him that dislocated his jaw and sent him to the floor. He hadn't seen it coming, and was in no condition to fight back. He was still in pain from it now several weeks later, but didn't want any treatment for that. In the condition he was in at his court appearance, it had seemed a better option to try something new like Emotional Logic, rather than go back to prison in such a vulnerable state.

I gained the impression, as we spoke back and forth about his life, that he was an intelligent person who had learnt to survive by being aggressive. He wasn't part of the drug-dealing mayhem that had been going on in the city, where gangs had been trying to make a police no-go area. In fact, he despised drugs. He simply enjoyed winning. That was the only way he knew how to have friends. I made up my mind to refer him to learn Emotional Logic from one of our leading tutors, David, a brilliant youth and systemic caseworker. Although he normally sees people in the 16-22 age range, and Steve was older, David has a way with language that reaches the hardest of hearts, and he understands the consequences of family dynamics better than most.

Four weeks or so later Steve reappeared in my consulting room. He immediately said, without further introduction, 'Doc, I've got it!'

I looked at him with a silent gaze of curiosity, then invited him to tell me more.

He said, 'That Doc you sent me to see is brilliant!' I nodded my agreement, not needing to correct the detail that David is not a 'Doc' but a systemically-trained practitioner. 'We got onto the subject of Bargaining – aggressive, passive, assertive. Walking down the street afterwards, I suddenly realised that *everyone I passed* is Bargaining all of the time to get back something they miss. You just have to work out what they are Bargaining for. And…' - here he raised both his fists in front of his chest - 'I realised for the first time that I don't *need* to use *these* to Bargain. I think this is brilliant! I want all my gang to learn Emotional Logic!'

David said afterwards that he hadn't done or said anything differently to his usual approach. He had affirmed Steve's emotions about his upbringing, and given a feedback explanation that fitted those unpleasant emotions into a logical process of adjusting to losses, each emotion having its useful purpose as part of moving that process on. Steve had then been quick to start naming his hidden losses, things in his past that had been important that he had either lost, or felt he had never had. He was retelling the story of his upbringing, but using the new language of loss constructively straight away.

We lost contact with Steve shortly after that. He was evicted from his accommodation for having failed to pay rent in the past. However, it was clear to David by then that his approach to managing the frustrations of his former way of life had completely changed. We hoped it would see him through this further setback.

All this was an affirmation of Emotional Logic's approach to anger management developed by Trisha Horgan, a Community Psychiatric Nurse-Therapist who has used Emotional Logic for two decades. She would say paradoxically to people diagnosed with personality disorder, 'You do Anger really well. Congratulations! Now, what about some of these other Stepping Stones? Might they also help you?' Trisha also developed our Emotional Logic approach to post-traumatic stress disorder, discovering how it is *not* necessary to revisit the traumatising past in order to learn how to move on constructively from it.

One feature of Steve's life that may have helped him to make this rapid adjustment to assertive Bargaining was his confident sense of belonging with his gang. As a leader, he didn't have to conform to someone else's rules, so he had little to lose by changing the rules unless the gang rebelled. Steve therefore had both a relational safe place, and a safe frame of mind from which to plan and make his adjustments to life. In Chapter 11 we shall see the sad consequences if these types of safe place are lacking in people's lives.

I'm reminded of another story here, on the same theme of *hostile* Bargaining, which can be either aggressive or passive to recover something but at the expense of the relationship. It is a very different situation about someone Marian met when out and about. She'll tell the story.

Marian tells a different but parallel story

Esther was part of an older person's club – a very different age to Steve. The club organisers had asked for a series of short teaching sessions on the useful purposes of the grief emotions. The second session was about Anger and Guilt and their unexpected place in a healthy adjustment process – to prevent the loss of something valued.

Afterwards, Esther pulled me aside, away from the throng enjoying tea and biscuits, and sat me down in a quiet corner, saying she needed my help. She explained, at some length, that her husband's dementia meant she was rarely able to leave him, painfully restricting her previously active social nature. 'It's terrible! This meeting is the only one in the week that I can get to.' Plenty of losses there, I was thinking, as the sense of injustice and bitterness became increasingly evident.

I started to interject that naming her hidden losses might lead to an action plan. However, Esther skilfully brought in a new complaint and kept to her own agenda by telling me that life at home was even more difficult, verging on chaotic, since her husband's young niece, Emily, had moved in. She was a shy, nervous girl, 'a bit flaky', and did not feel ready to live on her own or to share with others. That week, Emily had then announced that she was also leaving her job as a carer because she was being bullied.

The story went on, but not about the bullying. Esther had had hopes that Emily would help in the home, but then frustratedly said, 'She has no common sense at all! For example, after being repeatedly shown how to load the dishwasher correctly, and still getting it wrong, she has started leaving the dirty crockery on the work surface!'

I was beginning to feel frustrated with the detail, but I decided to ask how she had responded. Esther did admit that she had raised her voice on occasions. 'I was so disappointed; I could have screamed!'

Meanwhile, in the meeting room the tea things were being cleared away, and I really could have done with a cup of tea – my safe place, which I was increasingly feeling the need of. Esther had not finished, however. She wanted to explain about some complex financial arrangements to do with Emily's lodging. She then mentioned that Emily was with her husband now, reading to him, which he loved. I had begun to feel manipulated, and now assertively decided to take this opportunity to get a word of response in. Speaking firmly, I reframed this part of Esther's story as noticing that Emily had enabled her to come to this meeting, as well as bringing pleasure to her husband. Esther seemed almost ready to hear me, hesitating as she looked at me.

I could see that I would need to be very assertive to help Esther to move on from her 'poor old me' stance. I had noticed my Anger Stepping Stone appearing, so knew that I needed to prevent some personal loss. It had something to do with tea and biscuits, as well as the opportunity to talk to others, who were now putting their coats on. Maybe this Anger energy enabled me to move on to an even more assertive type of Bargaining than is my usual approach. I needed to recover my role also as a teacher of healthy adjustment processes. Instead of continuing to look at Esther's own losses, I turned to face her straight on and suggested that she start to make two guessed 'loss lists', one for her husband and one for Emily.

At that point, I said that I really must speak to the group organiser before she left and, wishing her success, I left her sitting, looking a little stunned. I joined the group saying their goodbyes, and managed a little time to talk among the thank yous. I briefly visited my Guilt Stepping Stone on the way home. Had I been un-empathic? No, I decided, others in the story also needed empathy – and so did I!

The next time I saw Esther was about a month later. She came rushing up to me, beaming. 'Thank you so much for being so firm with me. I realised, on doing as you suggested, how much more my husband has lost than I have. It has given me a whole new perspective! Oh, and Emily has found a new job and plans to move into a flat in two weeks. We still don't have an easy relationship, but that's okay. It will probably improve when we are not living together. My husband will miss her, though. Perhaps I should invite her for Sunday lunch sometimes. Then she can read to him. I do find doing that myself so boring, as he never remembers what was read before. Maybe he just likes her quiet, gentle voice…'

Trevor brings these stories together to conclude

How could this be a parallel story to Steve's? Curiously, when people feel manipulated, it usually means that the other person is using a passive style of Bargaining. They are not directly saying what they mean, but trying to control a situation anyway. This can generate angry and guilty feelings in others, which is why some people call it a passive-aggressive style of Bargaining. However, as you will see, we prefer to think of passive-aggressive as mixing different methods from the two outer lists of Bargaining styles (see page 168).

Now this is where these two stories are parallels to each other. Both aggressive and passive styles of Bargaining tend to break relationships in order to recover some 'thing'. They are both equally *hostile*. By breaking relationships they generate further losses, so situations tend to deteriorate even though 'the desired thing' might be successfully recovered. Manipulative and aggressive hostile Bargainers may then equally lose their main purpose in the confusing loss feelings that accompany apparent success. In such a state they never recognise or name what it is that they are still missing in life, but they carry on with what they are doing anyway. This is how despots grow.

The situations for both Steve and Esther turned around completely, however, when each was suddenly jolted out of their own feelings and ideas into considering the hidden losses previously unnamed for other people. For Steve it happened walking down the street. For Esther it happened when she was at home sitting at a table having decided she would write the two lists.

True empathy is *not* about feelings. That is sympathy. True empathy is about guessing or knowing the personal values that are generating people's feelings. Then a truly empathic person can respond with small compassionate acts to preserve the life-enhancing values.

Chapter 11

At a drop-in centre for street sleepers

Trevor tells the story

Torquay is famous as a British holiday 'riviera', with its pleasant climate, protected sea bay, history, cliffs and caves, beaches and theatre, palm trees and gardens. Consequently, its warm environment has also attracted a number of people who prefer to sleep rough, for whatever reason, or who are very poor and live on state benefits. The more run-down areas are tucked away.

There was plenty of support around for the less well off, and amongst that was a church known as St Mary Mags, for St Mary Magdalene, where each week it opened its café as a drop-in centre for street sleepers. Free bacon butties and tea, a chance to talk with people who showed an interest, showers, and perhaps new clothes to exchange, were all on offer. Three of our Emotional Logic tutors contributed their time voluntarily there. They wondered whether our lifelong-learning method could be adapted to meet the needs of this unsettled population, who carried many hurts that kept them on the move. And so started a nine-month voyage of discovery and new insights.

For just a few mornings we set up a two-metre wide canvas Turning Points diagram in a corner of the hall, and our trained volunteers would have brief conversations with the men and women who were passing through or waiting and resting there. They would hand them a set of Stepping Stones cards and ask them to show how they were feeling about life, or about situations they faced. Our experience elsewhere had been that learning even just one small thing about how unpleasant emotions fit into a healthy adjustment process could help to relieve people's tension and reduce their isolation or conflict with others.

It was all very informal, so anecdotal feedback was the rule of the day. Often teaching conversations were interrupted when the call went out that this person's bacon roll was ready, or it was their turn for a shower. We would never know if it made any difference to most, but it made a difference to us, and to at least two of those who chose to find out more. I'll tell their stories in a minute, but I'll start with the insight we gained.

You may have noticed that the card patterns shown in Marian's Emotional Logic Casebook tend to have the cards mostly spread out, perhaps in lines, and showing a time sequence as the person demonstrates how they adjusted to a situation over time. Well, it was different here. Almost invariably, the itinerant or resource-poor person would look through the seven cards in their hands and then throw one down, then another on top of it, and another on top of that, and so on until a stack of cards tightly knit together appeared in which it was not possible to see what was hidden inside (see Figure 11.1 as an example).

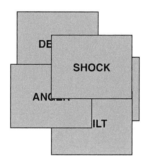

Figure 11.1 – An example of a street-sleeper card pattern

We have an absolute rule that you must NEVER touch the cards laid down by someone else in a pattern. They feel it as a personal intrusion, and may even swipe your hand away if you try. That makes it quite frustrating to wonder what is hidden at the bottom of the stack, and therefore in the depths of this person's heart. After seeing the pack thrown down like this by so many different people, I started to talk about 'the Big Four'. The stack patterns almost invariably included Shock, Anger,

Guilt and Depression. They always excluded Bargaining and Acceptance, the two growth points offering a way out of problems. The Denial card was variably in or out of the pattern, making a 'Big Five' if in, with the Denial making it more likely that emotional reactions would be explosive when these people connected with situations that 'pressed their emotional buttons'.

I had made that rule about not touching people's card patterns following an incident early on when Professor Sylvia Downs had been helping us to develop the cards. I had been seeing a girl who was school refusing, together with her mum. She had laid down just such a stack, and I had responded by saying, 'Thank you. That helps me to see how you are handling your emotions. It looks like you are holding them all in and not showing them to others, but they all have useful purposes to help you move on in life. I would like to help you to see those useful purposes. So, If we separate one emotion from another...' And here I reached forward and moved her top emotion card sideways to demonstrate what I meant. As I did so, her pupils, eyebrows and eyelids all dilated wide with terror as she tensed and froze. It was a visual lesson I have never forgotten. I apologised to her and her mum, and started the long process of trying to recover her trust.

So with these adults at the drop-in centre, we only *pointed to* the Turning Points diagram. We might walk over to it and talk about some of the useful purposes. Not uncommonly it would open a conversation about some past hurtful events. I gained the impression that these people had accumulated decades of unresolved grieving, probably from early childhood for many. It was like a post-traumatic stress disorder following more extended periods of time without any safe places. If that overload of simultaneous emotions had been their experience from an early age, perhaps now they were unable to separate out mentally one emotion from another. Their memories would always confuse them together. Their whole chaotic emotional history could be re-enacted in a flash when facing new situations that demanded a response.

Many of these people would have been diagnosed by professional services as having personality disorders. Their unpredictable or very restricted patterns of behaviour were inexplicable in simple terms of society's commonly understood relational responsiveness. Lack of emotional diversity would also reduce the capacity for choice, and therefore reduce the ability to take responsibility, which for most of the settled population is considered a normal feature of everyday life. Multiple loss reactions that had accumulated into unrecognised and unresolved grieving had thus *isolated* these people. No matter how much they might crave relationships, they were trapped from within.

These conversations were taking place in that hall some years before the research by Feliti and Anda in the USA brought the notion of adverse childhood experiences (ACEs) into centre stage in the UK. This research has broken the narrow and rigid 'diagnostic approach' to illnesses and personality disorders that for decades had focused professional interventions for difficult behaviour. Four or more ACEs can lead to a lifetime of difficulties with attachments and adjustments. Did respecting their traumatic grief, and teaching about the useful purposes of their unpleasant loss emotions, make any difference to these drop-in centre people back then? Well it certainly did to two of them.

Two determined ladies, independently of each other, saw reason to hope that they could understand this adjustment process.

Greta's story and what it led to

One I shall call Greta. She lived alone in a block of council flats and she troubled neighbours and many others with her explosive anger. Her Stepping Stones card pattern looked a bit like that shown in Figure 11.2.

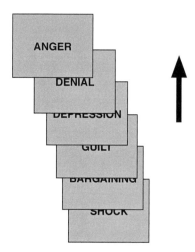

Figure 11.2 – Greta's Stepping Stones card pattern

The surprise was to see her Bargaining card right near the base of this eruption of anger. Whatever that attempt at Bargaining had been, it was followed by Guilt and Depression before being swallowed into the black hole of Denial. From there the whole tumultuous chaos of her emotional energy burst out like a volcano.

Greta joined a number of workshops that we were doing in that area. Bit by bit her story emerged, and with it her confidence grew to examine her styles of Bargaining, to reflect, and to learn that she had choices. As the Emotional Logic coaches who met her along the way began to recognise and understand the complexity of her grieving, we – and she – could see how she was reacting, but over-reacting possibly, to the outrageous behaviour of others around her. She was not purely generating it all from within herself.

We discussed in detail at one workshop how she might select from the assertive Bargaining list 'write a letter' to the resident of the flat above her, who was sweeping dog mess onto her balcony when no pets were allowed in the flats. When we met several weeks later and I asked, she said, 'It didn't make a jot of difference to her, but it did to me! I'm handling things differently now. In the past I'd have smashed her door down, and then I'd have the Council on me. Life's not good, but it could be a lot worse.'

As the Emotional Logic tutors reflected about what they were encountering, the idea emerged of 'fleeting whirlpools of loss emotions'. We had noticed in other situations how overlaps of two cards, or two columns of ticks on Loss Reaction Worksheets, could be associated with recognisable behaviours diagnosable as anxiety states, fatigue states, confusions, compulsive disorders, various types of depression, socially disruptive or destructive behaviour, and so on. These were maladaptive grief responses to stressful life circumstances, twisting an otherwise healthy adaptive process into something unhealthy. These responses to situational stresses or memories could become stable *habits of emotional processing* over time, in which case they could produce a consistent pattern of feelings – which psychologists would call symptoms – and behaviours – which psychologists would call signs. Thus, habitual maladaptive grief could be labelled or diagnosed as a range of common mental illnesses.

However, here at the drop-in centre we were seeing something else. The maths of it was simple but enlightening. If *three* cards were laid down overlapping each other in a card pattern, there were three potential pairings of them. That meant that the effects of any of the three different whirlpools might appear, so that feelings and behaviours might vary considerably as one or another whirlpool or turbulent eddy of emotional energy became dominant at any time. So if Shock, Guilt and Anger were laid overlapping, for example, then a person might experience shame (Shock-Guilt), feeling odd and out of it (Shock-Anger), and obsessional thoughts or behaviour (Anger-Guilt) in any mixture. Flipping temporarily and unpredictably between these could create an unstable mental state, which might present, for example, as an obsessive jealousy, or even paranoia if people imagined that others knew the cause of their shame. A person's behaviour and feelings could 'flit' between them all in an unstable manner. People could become unpredictable and unknowable, even to themselves. But that was 'the grieving me'. By understanding grief in a more constructive way, a more fulfilled personal identity could emerge.

And if the Big Four were all in a stack, potentially there were six pairs. So therefore the effects of six whirlpools could all fleetingly affect a person's experience of life. Their behaviour and their inner world identity might be in turmoil simultaneously. Denial would simply act as a pressure cooker in these circumstances, so that when it was no longer possible to ignore what was going on, out it all would come in a magnified torrent or jet that got labelled 'personality disorder'.

This is how the seed was discovered that has grown over time into Emotional Chaos Theory. It is a totally new way to understand the roots and the potential healing of mental illnesses and socially disruptive behaviour, based in a medical view of emotions as physical and social (social physiology). Chaos Theory is misnamed, however. It is a journalistic sound bite that does not convey the importance of its key feature, which is that this New Science way to understand turbulence also explains *how order can emerge out of chaos by feedback learning*.

We now have the proven benefit of Emotional Logic tools that can map the inner emotional chaos out of which common mental illnesses and socially disruptive behaviour emerge. That map empowers and guides people to explore, and to discover a uniquely relevant learning pathway, which will lead them to make wise decisions and action plans that build more stable, responsive and empathic relationships.

The development of Emotional Chaos Theory had help from an unexpected source. I was leading a workshop at which an uneven number of participants meant that I joined in a practical card-laying exercise. I paired up with someone I knew, and happened to trust. The exercise was for one person to mention a small issue that they had needed to adjust to, for the other then to practise handing over the cards and giving instructions on how to lay them out, and for them both then to use the four-question card-pattern analysis method to describe the pattern. This person handed me the cards, and instantly the small issue I'd chosen disappeared from my mind. I found myself laying out a pattern for how I felt when I remembered my childhood home.

Now, I am not going to become all morbid about this, but there were many ways in which it had been highly stressful. I was brought up with (and survived) older twin brothers, one of whom was very violent from an early age and who went on to be a paranoid schizophrenic in and out of mental hospitals. He terrorised staff and residents alike there, as he had done to us at home. The other twin had a physical disability with epilepsy. The two of them fought ceaselessly and violently. My parents did a heroic job staying together with all this chaos, but it took its toll on them also in many ways. I survived by hiding away psychologically, and physically sometimes, becoming hypervigilant and 'locked in' emotionally. I coped with profound shame, confusion and anger by containing it in Denial behind my studies. I also concealed it behind having a strong sense of wit, and having a means of transport always available to get away. It was not a good basis to learn how to build relationships. The card pattern I laid down came out as shown in Figure 11.3. Perhaps readers can recognise some features in it.

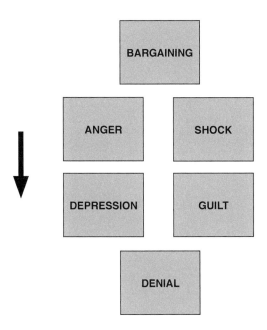

Figure 11.3 – Trevor's childhood home card pattern

I am forever Bargaining, and putting my true feelings into Denial. By using the cards, I suddenly saw for the first time *inside myself*, to where my feelings of instability and inner doubts came from. When I later learnt about Feliti and Anda's research findings, I counted up and realised I had a four-ACE background! Having noticed the Big Four neatly spaced out, I realised how this pattern showed how I *could* think about them separately, but I was able to see all six whirlpools fleetingly affecting my own life. I could see more clearly how they affected Marian's life, and troubled other's (for which I now eternally apologise!). It was a remarkable experience. Suddenly, I was getting to know myself better, being taught by the very method that I was using to teach others.

As a consequence, I realised that all I needed to do to accelerate my personal development was to replace my Denial card with my Acceptance card, and keep the others spaced out, recognising each of the emotional Stepping Stones as they arose in my experience, not allowing them to overlap. An example of how that feels comes from a lady whose chronic fatigue had improved by activating her Emotional Logic. She described the experience as the difference between having her emotions in a fast-spin tumble drier, and pegging them out on a line to dry in the breeze. This is why we say that being mindful of your emotions is the starting place for Emotional Logic, but activating your Emotional Logic moves you on from there to explore life.

Acceptance had not figured in my life strategy at all up to that point. After starting to work on accepting various hidden losses, now named, I noticed how my relationships began to improve. And so I have discovered it to be true in my own life, that when used constructively for specific named losses, Accepting and letting go of some things, and recognising my limits, can empower an even greater exploratory nature of the Growth Cycle. Even so, some emotional whirlpool habits do take time and relational consistency to change. Marian can now spot me 'going down my favourite whirlpool', and say something helpful that reminds me I don't have to go there. I have the power of choice. So, thank you to that person who passed me the Stepping Stones cards so effectively!

Sandra's story

Now we can get back to the story of the second lady I am going to tell you about, whom we met through the drop-in café at St Mary Mags. I shall call her Sandra. She, like me, was Bargaining *all* the time to keep her life contained and moving forward. Her intense Bargaining had its own price in terms of tension and anxieties. Coming from a multiple ACE background, she had missed out on a lot of education, which she had already decided before we met was her life goal to recover. Despite severe dyslexia, she had successfully gained a qualification at evening classes. When she saw what we were bringing to the café, and tried out the cards, she wanted it. She asked to sign up to train as an Emotional Logic coach.

We never went into great depth about the events of her early life. It simply wasn't necessary. It would have disrupted her life-development focus. Instead, we helped her to develop a habit of naming what she had lost or missed out on as a result of bad things happening to her. She then learnt to recognise these named losses as her personal values. After that, she was quick to develop her own strategies to recover whatever she chose to prioritise.

Sandra was full of surprises. She attended workshops, talked with others, and sent their card patterns for interpretation, emailed coursework, had telephone tutorials, and slowly, slowly edged her way to success at being able to describe and explain to others the healthy adjustment process, using the various tools and information sheets. Along the way she came to her own conclusion that she wouldn't pretend she was going to become a full coach, able to help people to untangle complex life problems. She became confident, however, and so did we, that she knew how to be a change facilitator for other people as well as herself. She could talk with anyone, anywhere, and open doors in their life by taking out her Stepping Stones cards from her handbag and saying, 'That sounds bad, I know, but don't tell me how you feel. Use these cards to show me how you feel…'

Chapter 12

De-radicalisation, trafficking and multiple shootings

This chapter illustrates the potentially disastrous social impact of the Anger-Depression whirlpool on individuals and society. People who have discovered how to manipulate this emotional whirlpool in others for their own gain can have a painfully destructive effect on human nature. The solution we offer is described here and in Chapter 14.

At all ages, learning to activate one's inbuilt Emotional Logic empowers people to resist manipulation by assertively saying 'No' when their intuition alerts them that behind offers of gain lurk hidden motives of control. Unpleasant loss emotions may appear as pre-verbal intuitions. By understanding how loss emotions have useful purposes to *enhance* life, people may be alerted and empowered to choose alternative strategies when the temptation in the short-term may be to give in to dubious offers of pleasure. If loss emotions are no longer seen as reasons to be hopeless, because their *adaptive purpose* is known, people can choose the longer view instead. They may be better equipped to name the personal values they want to build a future on, and to question the values of others.

The Active Change Foundation

In 2016, militant jihadist movements that abused Islamic teaching and unbalanced it to enhance their own political power were attracting fighters from around the world. The Taliban and Islamic State (ISIS) were most prominent, but Al-Shabab was also active in Kenya. I suspected that an Anger-Depression whirlpool was behind the willingness of some people to become suicide bombers, because I knew it could generate both destructive and suicidal drives. I had realised already that Emotional Logic could release people from those drives, and so I attended a de-radicalisation conference in London to see if I could interest anyone in this innovative approach to understanding the problem of radicalisation.

There I heard a speech from Hanif Qadir of the Active Change Foundation (ACF), a voluntary Islamic de-radicalisation charity based in North East London. Their volunteers went out onto the streets to talk with local gangs in the evenings. This was the preventive level at which I thought Emotional Logic might be most effective. I spoke with Hanif afterwards, and later gave an introductory presentation to some of his team. This led on to coaching training for 20 Islamic and other volunteers and paid staff who, apart from doing the evening de-radicalisation work on the streets, also ran a gym and drop-in centre for the local community. Family support was a central feature of their work.

When they learnt about the effect of the Anger-Depression whirlpool, they affirmed that these two were the predominant emotions they were encountering on the streets. These emotions led to greater bonding into gangs, where people gained a sense of empowerment and safety by leaving behind their fear of isolation. They had never imagined, however, that the emotional chemistry of these two loss emotions could interact in such a way that it could also prime irrational intense outbursts of confrontational or destructive behaviour. I was suggesting to them that this behaviour was not a core feature of personality, but a learned pattern of grieving for multiple losses into which people could be manipulated. Because the emotional intensity of the whirlpool came from unrecognised and unnamed losses, which were personal values, this learned pattern could therefore be unlearned by helping people to name their losses without inducing a sense of shame. The ACF were interested. And they were in a position to shift attitudes.

Hanif and another leader, Mike, were involved also in work with imprisoned terrorists. Their role was to help them reconsider the Islamic theology into which their teachers of radicalisation had unbalanced them. I met Mike at a week-long leadership training event run by ACF to support potential young entrepreneurs in schools and colleges. Their personal development programme could identify at an early stage young people who were at risk of radicalisation. Mike was struck by my talk, in which I had explained to the hundred or so young people participating, how important it was to recognise loss emotions and attach them to specific named losses. Doing so could energise a constructive response to the loss, and so prevent whirlpools of loss emotions from forming that might generalise into an attitude towards life as a whole. I emphasised how these unpleasant emotions are the evidence that we have personal values. They move us to restore life, not break it up.

He and a police contributor spoke with me after, and keenly observed that Anger and Depression were the two key emotions also driving the convicted terrorists. Mike immediately grasped the notion that a whirlpool of emotional chemistry would prevent each of the constructive loss emotions fulfilling its healthy purpose, forcing the emotional tension to show as something else – destructive and suicidal drives – which could be directed by a charismatic leader to break up situations that their followers had come to believe were outrageous and had to change.

The shift from a healthy grieving adjustment process into an Anger-Depression whirlpool comes about when people start to believe that they are powerless to influence a situation that concerns them. Someone who then offers a clear and accessible solution that taps into the emotional energy at that point, can create a surge of interest and false hope, with reduced capacity for that person to rationally reflect and balance what is being said to them. It would sound something like, 'But if you join *my* gang... '

Suddenly, something new made sense to them. The professional de-radicalisation services had been mystified at their discovery of the amazing speed with which a new convert to a belief system (in this situation, a twisted form of Islam), could be radicalised into a terrorist who was willing to sacrifice their life for a cause. In some cases it would take only *two weeks*! Now here was an explanation in the emotional chemistry that shapes people's decisions with greater power than their reasoning.

The emotional chemistry of anger drives people outwards to take action to change something. The emotional chemistry of depressive emptiness drives them inwards to disengage from life and reflect on personal limits. The constructive useful purpose of the creative *Depression of loss* – as a place of decision in the Growth Cycle when seeing one's limits – can be fulfilling when it is focused on a single, named personal loss. It gets pulled out from the Growth Cycle, however, when the focus of attention shifts onto whole situations where multiple other losses confuse the capacity to make decisions. If the situation is broadened into 'life as a whole', then this way of thinking about limits may unhelpfully also generalise into, 'I'm useless at all this; and I always have been; and I'm useless at everything I try to do; so what's the point of trying anyway?' This is the root of 'learned helplessness', a way of thinking and feeling that manipulators can enhance and turn to their own advantage. One way they can do this is to raise within the person their *outwardly-moving anger* alongside their *inwardly-moving depressive feelings*. Then the rational part of the brain, the neocortex, cannot *orientate* its thinking, because the information it handles requires both inward and outward responses simultaneously. People get disorientated. They may feel 'in a spin' and isolated within their own mental worlds.

In the Anger-Depression whirlpool, the inner state of depressive emptiness creates a sense of powerless isolation. Externally-directed anger may then drive a desire to display power *by any means* to break up that potential inner state of despair. If someone plays on that sense of isolation, or even purposely generates or exacerbates it, they create a handle on someone else's life, and can move that person wherever they want for the manipulator's own gain.

Joining an army may feel empowering, like joining a very large street gang. Given a cause by a false or corrupt teacher, people driven into an Anger-Depression whirlpool can wreak havoc, and may sacrifice their lives willingly when they are deceived into believing they are empty and isolated when separated from the false teacher.

The *lie* believed is that every loss emotion is evidence of inner emptiness. In truth, it is not. Every loss emotion is evidence of having personal values! The problem is that they are not yet named. A list of hidden losses *written down* when activating someone's Emotional Logic is a list of that person's inner values. It tells a liberating story of who this person is. It maps their identity in this social world.

A close association developed between the Emotional Logic Centre and the Active Change Foundation, preparing their staff to teach Emotional Logic in schools to strengthen young people's capacity to resist manipulation, in London and elsewhere where they worked. That was, until the government cut off their funding. Some political drift had changed. The war against ISIS recruitment had begun to turn. The Active Change Foundation fell out of favour. The gym closed. The schools work stopped. The community support of families ground to a halt. Staff were made redundant, and the volunteers dispersed.

What can one say?

A lesson has been learnt about manipulation and how to resist it.

The same unbalancing dynamics can happen wherever in the world people turn to manipulative teachers who seek political power to dominate others. There is as much diversity with breakaway groups within the religion of Islam as there is in any other religion and in secular gatherings around beliefs and ideologies, where *teachers* have emotional sway in people's developing lives. Emotional Logic helps to see how the vast majority of people drawn into violence to promote a narrow ideology are swayed into behaviours that they later regret *by a few people manipulating their unrecognised grieving*. The same is true of conspiracy theorists, who undermine good sense.

The big lesson learnt through our association with the Active Change Foundation is how to see through to the grieving heart of people whose behaviour is disruptive, and then to discover if there are teachers in the background misleading them. It is not just a matter of confronting one ideology with another, or of early detection of mental illness, or of blaming personality disorders. It is a matter of casting a light on deception and how to resist it emotionally by *knowing* about healthy emotional adjustment and the potential for growth in small areas of personal life. Having heard the obvious losses and hidden values, such as unemployment, that lead to honest grief troubling people's hearts, it is important to respond with at least a small compassionate act, and if possible to provide choices that promote life. That's what the Active Change Foundation had started to do on the streets of North East London.

Grooming and trafficking

While I and others in the Emotional Logic Centre had been engaging with these de-radicalisation events, Marian had become equally concerned with a different area of life. Kris Hollington's book, *Unthinkable: The Shocking Scandal of the UK Sex Traffickers* had been published (Simon & Schuster, 2013). Marian started exploring how Emotional Logic might help victims of sexual abuse, where highly complex hurts created an unstable inner emotional state that made consistent learning difficult. With grooming and trafficking, however, we realised that another dimension was added to the radicalisation problem.

Girls in their early teens from stable homes, as well as from disrupted ones, were being drawn into a way of life as sex slaves, and they were willingly returning to their abusers when removed. This led to the classic response from the professional fostering and criminal justice systems that this was a personality problem. These teenage girls, they said, were exercising their free will. No-one, no responsible adult, had a right to restrict their freedom of choice.

Rubbish!

Where had *this* lie come from? Kris Hollington's book (and there are others on the market on similar subjects) contains a remarkable short chapter (Chapter 32) that provides a profound insight. An anonymous caseworker, working with ex-offenders, who had the same brave character as those from the Active Change Foundation, was working to rehabilitate a young man who had been a leading groomer for a trafficking gang in the North West of England. The young man regretted his actions now, and although described as 'a hideous man' in that book, was willing to give an interview to explain how he had worked, with a view to preventing others repeating it.

The caseworker had explained to the interviewer, while waiting to meet this man, that 'grooming' was the wrong concept if it is imagined to mean simply softening someone up to temptation. To quote: 'That stuff is amateur in comparison to what these gangs are trying to achieve. They're playing a long game. What they want to do is socially engineer a girl into a relationship, so that she'll remain loyal to them, no matter what, even after her parents know. So, by that time, it's already too late.' The chapter goes on with many insights that I would not have space to repeat here. A key feature that I would like to draw out clearly, though, is how the strategy depends entirely on putting a wedge between a daughter and her parents. Many of the girls come from already disrupted families, and are living with carers or in hostels. But whether with employed carers, or natural parents, the method is the same. At the empty heart of this cruel and tragic strategy is *generating a sense of isolation at critical moments*.

The social engineer, the corrupter, also abuses the concept of *a safe place to plan* during loss reactions. By enhancing small differences between the daughter and her parents, making the daughter feel a sense of outrage at her parents' behaviour or responses, the manipulator can present himself as an alternative safe relationship. The places he goes then become alternative safe places, and the people he meets come to be seen as safe people because the groomer says so. This concept of a safe place is vital to the corrupting strategy.

Manipulation moves to another level once the notion of safety is established in the girl's mind. The deceptive relationship is established amid lots of fun, music, alcohol and drugs over several months. Having increased her anger during this time against her parents, or any other secure feature of her life, and having shared gifts and money, the manipulator then deeply shocks and disappoints her. He says she has behaved in a way that upsets him, but does not explain what she has done wrong. She is left isolated and angry against *all* whom she believes have abandoned her, doubting her ability to understand what she could do differently. Self-questioning creates an overload of grief with no way out.

That sounds to me like leaving her in a whirlpooling chaos of simultaneous Anger-Depression, and Shock-Guilt, the Big Four again, all happening at once in a mental place of lonely isolation. Destructive and self-destructive shame swirl around.

So then the hideous manipulator says, 'I want you back, and I want you to let a friend of mine come into you. He needs you.' We do not need to go any further along the destructive path of distorted humanity that follows and escalates. The manipulator becomes her only safe place.

A lot of work and consistency are involved in creating an alternative safe place for a young person who has been so emotionally corrupted and taught such false beliefs. But some do manage to leave. Others die.

It is hard, when overcoming Denial that such things happen, not to become convinced that pure evil exists in this world. I have thought long and hard about that archaic word. It is banished from experimental psychology, so 'reasonable' people don't talk about it. In some religious settings the notion of evil is overused, or stylised so that it becomes embarrassing to talk about it. So how do we talk about the manipulators and false teachers who corrupt this world and lead humanity into death from life?

May I offer my resulting beliefs for you to reject or work with as you feel best? If we return for a moment to the Introduction, Figure 0.1 is called 'The Life Cycle diagram'. It shows how the purpose of grieving is to explore new ways to reconnect with our values and the people and things we love. Grief is not the end of love. Grief is love in its recovery mode. In that mode, its unpleasantness is there to *move* us, urging us to explore how to restore the joy of love when change has pushed us out of a comfort zone. I believe that evil is the name given to the wilful choice someone makes to magnify someone else's grief out of proportion to the situations they face, and then to prevent that loss-related emotion from fulfilling its useful purpose to reconnect with true personal values or true other people. The evil intent is to block that top right-hand corner of the diagram. This leaves people isolated and distressed, with an emotional energy that a manipulator harnesses into a handle on that person's life. All of this is done simply to enhance the manipulator's own pleasure or gain. So therefore, evil is a personal choice. Almost anyone is potentially at risk of turning to evil temporarily when adverse life circumstances seem too challenging, when giving grief to others seems more appealing than bearing suffering themselves. But developing an evil heart is a step on from that.

This personal-choice view of evil also means that there is no need to postulate an esoteric, self-existent 'force of evil' that corrupts this world, as if in a battle with a force of good. These ideas are good for film entertainment, but not good as a guide to realistic action that resists the destructive impact of evil choices on others. Evil choice is a corruption of love, which is relational. It has no existence in and of itself. But if a person's character is to choose to remain evil, they potentially can be disempowered by those who *know that grief is not the end of love*. Understanding grief as adaptive inner transformation, leading to growing strength, removes the handles on a person's life that manipulators and false teachers might otherwise get hold of. Without that, they lose energy and will, and discover their own emptiness.

And finally, as the 'hideous man' has shown us, who was willing to be interviewed as part of his rehabilitation, people can regret their former choices and speak out words of life instead that might help others to avoid going down that same selfish route. When evil is seen as personal choices, made within specific contexts, even forgiveness may become possible when there is a change of heart.

Multiple shootings and stabbings leading to suicide

I am not going to exhaust your compassion by pointing out the obvious similarities of destruction and suicide by disgruntled multiple killers. Its current prevalence may be because a grudge can be manipulated out of proportion and in comparative isolation by false teachers on the Internet.

I am told by American friends who have learnt Emotional Logic that psychiatrists there repeatedly report Anger and Depression as the explosive mixture behind these tragic events. In the search for root causes and preventive strategies, Emotional Logic adds the medical physiology of whirlpooling emotional chemistry to the psychology of feelings and beliefs. Emotional adjustment and maladjustment run deeper, and are even more powerful than beliefs, to motivate destructive inner drives. To prevent these tragedies, our work in schools may help to prevent the individual isolation and disconnection that lurk behind these urges to mass trauma.

Chapter 13

The Kenyan prison chaplain

Trevor tells the story

In December 2007, vote-rigging in the Kenyan presidential election led to riots and violence that extended into 2008. Several politicians were violently ejected from their constituencies as tribal jealousies overtook democratic processes. One who lost his seat in this way was Mike Brawan, in Nakuru in the Rift Valley where some of the worst violence had occurred.

I first met Mike in 2008, following a phone call from friends in Cornwall who said he had arrived to recover from this major setback in his life and was staying with them. I was booked to run a day workshop there, and went a day early to meet him. Mike had risen from a traumatising family background in Nakuru that had led to him eventually having to live on the city rubbish dump for three years. Someone from a local church had found him, who knew him from before the time when his parents had been killed, and sponsored him through a university education. Mike had developed a strong advocacy for the poor during this time, having seen how people could be pushed into hardship through no fault of their own. In Kenya, Christianity is still a strong feature of community life, and Mike had become a pastor and church leader, in which role he ran various charitable projects that had given him wide support in the town. He had developed his political hopes to try to influence systems nationally, and had been voted in on his social justice platform.

But here he was, with his plans and hopes shattered. At the dining table in my friends' home, I talked through the Emotional Logic method with Mike and another guest from America. Mike used the Stepping Stones and feelings cards to map out the depth of his emotional turmoil. I was able to show how his pattern could be untangled into the energy to activate a new, values-based action plan.

He was amazingly quick to grasp the ideas, and to see the potential power of the method. He joined the workshop the following day, and… that was the last I saw of him for eight years. I had one report back a month later from my friends, saying that he had returned to Kenya, had used the Emotional Logic method there with another pastor's wife who had been insomniac with stress for over a year, and she had slept that night for the first time.

Restoration of a better sleep pattern is a change that I frequently encounter as an early sign of emotional untangling after learning to activate Emotional Logic. So in one personal learning session and one day workshop, Mike had clearly learnt enough to put his new understanding to good effect for the benefit of others.

Eight years later I received a phone call from Mike saying he was in the UK and wanted to come and see me. I met him the next day at our home, and was surprised when he announced that his purpose in travelling up from Cornwall was specifically to thank me. What for? I had turned his life around. The story that unfolded was so remarkable that Marian and I decided we had to travel to Kenya to check out the facts. The events he described after learning Emotional Logic seemed so unbelievable. We went a year later, taking several days out to see him while attending a conference in Nairobi. We discovered that all he had said was probably true, except that it had been understated…

In 2008 Mike had returned to Nakuru in the Kenyan Rift Valley to develop his church ministry. He became the chaplain to the men's maximum security prison in nearby Naivasha. That ministry went so well that he had been invited to take on other prisons, until he was responsible for about a third in the country. Mike had also introduced Emotional Logic in Swahili to his church and his charitable ministries, and then developed a Christian programme for the prisons that included Emotional Logic to help new inmates adjust to prison life. He had trained the long-stay prisoners, the lifers – many former murderers – as Emotional Logic facilitators who were able to have creative conversations that could help new arrivals not only to accept their new condition, but also to turn their emotions around into a hope for rehabilitation and renewal of their lives.

Emotional Logic explains forgiveness in terms of a giant leap from Anger about loss to the Acceptance that no single action can recover *all* the hidden losses that are associated with the situation. Not forgiving those people who have hurt you in the past may trap you in a damaging desire for revenge; and any act of revenge would also not recover all the losses. It would only further prevent you from exploring a new life with the emotional energy that is already churning inside.

The prisoners learnt about healthy loss and adjustment reactions, and splitting big situations down into small chunks. Each chunk was a named loss, then understood to be a named personal value. This was transformative for them, so that a conversational support process could be initiated towards Acceptance and letting go one by one of unhelpful named values while in prison, and planning to preserve helpful ones on release. The prisoners then found that this liberated their energy to explore something new.

That was where Mike's wider charitable rehabilitation programmes came in, both for those in prison, and for those in the communities where his church members had been released from lives of poverty, prostitution and crime. So much of the damaging behaviour that follows in society is born of unrecognised grieving. Mike was working at the root values to reverse this, not merely criticising the feelings and behaviours.

Prisoners found this process also set their hearts free from that inner prison of anger feelings, which many had carried for years when out in their so-called freedom. Instead, power had been recovered more constructively, as the power of choice to act not on feelings but on explicitly named values. All this could only be achieved through conversations with others who were in this similar situation, a cascading benefit within the prison community.

The transformation of prison life had been remarkable. Previously there had been two or even three suicides a week when facing the prospect of years in a maximum security prison. That dropped to only one or two a month. The reoffending rate for prisoners released had also fallen to virtually nil. We could not believe it, so we continued to question and doubt until we were taken into one of the prisons. Mike tried and failed to get us permission to enter the men's maximum security prison, but what happened to us in the women's prison in Nakuru makes us believe it was true.

We were taken in through the gates in a small group of people with Mike, who were all received joyously by the woman Prison Governor and her warders, with a sort of respectful gratitude. After introductions, it was clear that they had already heard of Emotional Logic, and the respect was extended to Marian and myself. We were shown around the undulating mud compound and low buildings, where more than 200 sombre, withdrawn women eked out their lives. The ones with the orange mark on the shoulder of their simple tunics were the lifers, the murderers.

We were invited to stir the huge vat in the open kitchen area where the privileged few had work to do preparing the simple mealie-meal maize flour porridge that is their staple diet. With sticks the size of rowing boat oars we could hardly move it. Nearby were huge water storage tanks. It turned out that Mike had bought them with donations from America, because the water supply had previously been erratic and unclean. The Governor and Mike were discussing how they would soon need another bowser lorry of water to restock them. He had also bought the mealie-meal, so clearly he had vastly improved the living conditions of the prisoners. He had introduced his Emotional Logic and Christian forgiveness programme here too.

The prisoners stood in small groups dispersed around the compound watching the party, blankly. Marian and I were invited to speak to them. We had imagined we would be invited to speak to the warders, so this was unexpected. Now Marian's skills quickly came to the fore, and she suggested to me that we did it as a role-play, with Marian acting as a convicted thief, and me introducing Emotional Logic to her. We had done role-plays before, so we knew how to tip bits of teaching in along the way.

Marian loves this sort of acting, and thrives on it, but half-way through there was so little reaction from the prisoners that I wondered if they understood what we were saying, and two thirds of the way through I began to lose confidence and whispered to Marian that perhaps we ought to abandon it and just explain the key points. However, Marian's safe place is getting out there! So, she firmly whispered back to me, somewhere between assertively and aggressively with a pleasant smile, to get on with it. I did.

At the end, there was silence. But then we noticed that the Prison Governor was looking a little troubled. She seemed to make a decision, then stepped forward and spoke loudly in English to the prisoners across the whole compound. 'Prisoners. I have learned something from this presentation. I have learned that grief leads to a Growth Cycle. In the past we have always based our prison programme on making you feel guilty for your crimes. But I state to you now, that in the future we shall base your rehabilitation programmes instead on getting you from Guilt to your Growth Cycles.'

There was *no* rapturous applause. How could there be? But among the visiting party there were smiles and nods. What happened next is emblazoned on Marian's and my minds. A group of about six women gathered into a huddle and started whispering to each other, two with orange tags. They came and stood in a row in front of the visiting team, and started dancing that slow, swinging, relaxed, repetitive dance that only Africans do as naturally as breathing. And they started singing. Without a cantor, they all sang in unison the same words, 'We are not going… to stay on… our Guilt Stepping Stones… too long… We are going… to move on… and on…'

Mike started dancing in response, that slow stepping, pan-Africa dance of stamping the left foot down in the same place every time, stepping forwards onto the right foot firmly pressed down to take the weight, then back onto the left and swinging the body back to place the right firmly behind, then forward again, and so on and on in a rhythmic walk of life that goes everywhere and nowhere simultaneously. And the song and the dance spread among the visiting party. The Prison Governor joined in, the warders, and more and more of the prisoners were joining, but not all. I started to feel out of place like a statue, and let the rhythm start to move me as well, and Marian joined also. 'We are not going… to stay on… our Guilt Stepping Stones… too long… We are going… to move on… and on…' It went on for at least 10 minutes, Mike's face beaming.

In England after an event we ask people to complete an evaluation form to give written feedback. Here we had a spontaneous song, dance and jubilation, which showed that we had been heard. We felt truly heard.

*

It would be easy to doubt Mike's influence in prison settings from just this one story. However, he did not let us sit idle, and the events of the three days that we had with him in the wider community showed us how extensively he was impacting the social issues of his home area, and beyond in East Africa. He achieved this by channelling active support from high-level business sponsorship groups in America.

We were whisked from place to place, and pushed forward to speak at this meeting and that. We ran Emotional Logic teaching at his huge church in the poor suburbs, where over a thousand come to Sunday services. We discovered that he is 'bishop' over more than 60 churches around Kenya – but then so many claim to be that. However, we discovered that it was true when Marian and I were set up to speak at a day conference for 300 church leaders and bishops. Emotional Logic speaks to the humanity of relationships behind any culture or religion. I had run reconciliation workshops between Jews and Arabs near Jerusalem, and with refugees in Jordan. To this audience I explained, sharing with Marian the presentation about the useful purposes of our unpleasant emotions, that the central figure of their church ministry was a man who showed perfect humanity in the way he related. And this man, Jesus of Nazareth, had experienced all these same emotions of loss, during his life and when approaching his torture and death. He had demonstrated how to harness them into a Godly walk that he knew would restore life for others, not steal it from them. Church leaders could start to respect their own and other people's emotions more if they wanted to reflect Jesus in their ministries.

We thought we were doing well until Mike came forward, grabbed the microphone out of my hand and started retelling the story, it seemed, in Swahili. We saw then his public speaking skills, how he moved the hearts of those many church leaders with both humour and challenges. He told us later that he had a TV show, and as a motivational speaker had conference bookings at which he taught Emotional Logic.

After that address to the church leaders, he asked Marian and I to take a pastor aside who had a particular problem with a neighbouring church, and Mike disappeared for a while. When we met later, he was ecstatic. He had just overseen a gathering of 20 pastors who for years had been undermining each other, and who had right now turned around and asked for forgiveness and reconciliation with each other. The gridlock he had worried about in lack of cooperation in the community was being broken.

We were driven out of the city to the mountainous rubbish dump that covers acres. It rises perhaps 200 feet above the countryside, where hundreds of people live by scratching from the trash. Mike showed us where on it he had lived for three years, after he, his four brothers and his sister had been orphaned by a car crash. One disaster after another had happened to them at the hands of extended family who should have looked after them, but abused them instead, so that all five were now dead and only he was still alive. Mike was greeted rightly as a hero in that outcast community as we arrived by car, climbing and bouncing over mud and rubbish. We were shown around the rough wooden school that he had built for the children who lived there. We saw the same huge water storage tanks that he had installed there, just as he had at the women's prison, to provide clean water and reduce disease. We were invited to buy hand-made craft items beautifully fashioned by some of the thin and wasted women out of the discarded rubbish that surrounded them as their natural lived environment.

And then it turned out that Mike was not only famous here, on the city rubbish tip. I caught sight of his passport once, and he saw me looking at it. On the front was a golden spear. He explained that the 'Order of the Burning Spear' in Kenya is equivalent to being honoured for services to society with an OBE in the United Kingdom. He travelled abroad as a VIP, waved through customs because of that passport. He had maintained his political friendships with the leading politicians of

Kenya and the East African Union and he had shared Emotional Logic with them privately, helping them to harness their emotions constructively as they struggled to manage insoluble problems on the scale of nations.

Figure 13.1 – Mike

Something similar had happened among those who supported him in America. Mike had been taught his motivational speaker skills by an American. His financial support came from large churches in the USA, which he diverted not into luxuries, but into… Another surprise… We were driving along one street in Nakuru where a long wall hid a thriving market with many craft and food stalls. Mike had bought that market, and through it he had set up micro-economic projects for people who were leaving behind street lives of crime and prostitution. He had a particular and honouring concern for the prostitutes, because of the abuse his sister had suffered before she died. He was moved by brotherly love in all he did. He had a deep understanding of human nature, but was not defeated by human nature. He had seen hope win through, and he continued to spread it. It is called post-traumatic growth.

When we arrived in Nakuru, Marian and I had planned to mix a bit of holiday with business, intending to visit the game park on the edge of the town. After a couple of hectic days, Mike realised how disappointed Marian was not to have been able to get there, given the programme he had arranged. On the third day a young woman on a 50cc motorbike pulled up. She spoke with Mike and his team, then came over and asked Marian to put on the spare helmet she carried. Mike came beaming over and explained. She was a former prostitute who had set up a business as a 'boda-boda boy'. Young men with these small motorbikes were seen all over the place as the local taxi service. Marian was being offered a great privilege, to have a free ride with the first-ever female boda-boda boy. Full of trepidation, but not wanting to disappoint, Marian slipped on the helmet, grabbed the small handle in front of the pillion seat, and was whisked away with a somewhat inward-looking attempt at a smile in her eyes, or was it an appeal?

Fifteen minutes later they were back, with Marian in a hilarious mood. Her boda-boda girl had taken her to the entrance gate of the game reserve, and brought her straight back, just so that Marian could say that she had been there! Taken for a ride.

*

Back in England, Mike sent us a video from the men's maximum security prison. Two hundred men in striped fatigues were dancing the same sort of dance we had seen at the women's prison, and singing. Apparently, they were singing thanks to us.

Of course, the culture is different here in the UK. We made attempts to get EL into two prisons. The response was to ask that we prepare it as a training course with educational credits, as the men liked to pick up qualifications. When we tried to do that, the week's programme was too full to fit another course in.

'We are not going… to stay on… our Guilt Stepping Stones… too long… We are going… to move on… and on…' I remain an eternal optimist.

Chapter 14

Keeping hopeful – our work in schools

'If only I'd learnt this 20 years ago!' 'All children should learn this!' These are the sorts of comments adults commonly make when they get their lightbulb moment, when they see all their unpleasant emotions as not negative but having useful purposes to move life on. So here is the story of how we moved Emotional Logic on from its medical, health and social care background into an educational setting, where prevention truly could be better than cure.

There are two strands to the story. The first is how I came to accept that teachers in secondary schools (high school) were serious when they said that if a child was anxious or depressed on transition from primary education, they could face a whole school career of mental health problems. We needed to prevent problems in primaries by improving adaptability for the transition.

The second is the story of the Butterfly Effect development of our work in primary and secondary schools that I call, with Carly's permission, "What's happened to Carly?!" A Butterfly Effect is a term from chaos theory that explains how big changes can follow from a small incident. A serendipitous encounter re-started our whole schools programme at a time when we could see no way into a closed and highly stressed system. A Butterfly Effect is like a ripple effect, but it describes a deeper transformation of life, or a more colourful one, as if a cloud has passed and the ripples spreading on a lake are suddenly bathed in glorious sunlight.

Secondary schools early on

Staff at the local community college in the south Devon town where I had my medical practice noticed that after learning Emotional Logic some teenagers had been able to stop self-harming. The Principal gave his support for the lead of their behavioural support team and an attendance officer to learn Emotional Logic. We agreed a scheme whereby they would attend our general workshops, and then sit in with me apprentice-style for a morning a week at the college, where I would see three youngsters referred for behavioural support for 40-minute learning sessions, weekly for four weeks. This would enable them to apply the general method of Emotional Logic to the specific problems the teachers were encountering. Because I was teaching the child a conversational skill, the option was open with the child's agreement to invite in a parent or close friend or family member for any of the sessions. Then, all present would learn to interpret unpleasant emotions in the same constructive way, as important parts of a healthy adjustment process to life's challenges.

The lead teacher and attendance officer watched in those appointments how I adjusted the lifelong-learning method to the individual. Then, for the next four weeks, I watched them as they led the personalised teaching appointments.

The attendance officer sadly moved to another job, which is a problem that affects many new projects. However, over the next three years the behavioural support service lead continued, seeing 51 young people aged 13 to 15, consistently recording their feedback comments. None had refused to follow this learning approach. It is a valuable part of the story to show his summary of pupils' comments, made before he retired:

Table 14.1: 'Have you noticed any difference in schoolwork, or the way you feel about school?'

Work-related comments	Number of comments	% of comments
Concentrate better	17	31%
Working better	11	20%
Doing the work (progressed)	6	11%
Getting good notes	4	7%

Getting on better	3	6%
Try harder	2	4%
Pay more attention	2	4%
More focused	2	4%
Listen more	2	4%
Eager to work	1	2%
Don't give up	1	2%
Attending more of my lessons	1	2%
Spend more time on work	1	2%
Committed	1	2%
Total comments	**54**	**100%**

Feelings-related comments	**Number of comments**	**% of comments**
Calm, more relaxed	6	22%
Happier going to school	6	22%
Feel better (good, easier)	4	15%
Confident	3	11%
Happier person	3	11%
Less stressed	3	11%
Enjoy school now (which is really weird!)	2	7%
Total comments	**27**	**99%**

Social-behaviour-related comments	**Number of comments**	**% of comments**
Better with friends	4	25%
Don't get angry (upset)	3	19%
Behaviour better	3	19%
Don't get into fights	2	13%

More patience	1	6%
Don't shout out so much	1	6%
Better attitude	1	6%
No longer hide behind a false face	1	6%
Total	**16**	**100%**

Grand Total of comments 100
Comments reflecting positive change 97
Nothing changed 3
Comments reflecting negative change 0

The effectiveness and acceptability of the teaching method for young people was now clear. Behaviour and academic performance improved. This community college held planning meetings for the Year Heads and the pastoral team at which referral criteria were agreed that explicitly sought a balance between the need for discipline and the need for pastoral support. In this way, both the 'hawks' and the 'doves' in the teaching staff felt heard and included in the whole-school approach.

We tried replicating this in two other secondary schools, but ran into problems with financial planning priorities in both of the Senior Management Teams. This showed us the importance of 'buy-in' from the Principal to push through something that did not seem initially to be directly related to the curriculum, even though the results had shown benefits for schoolwork performance and commitment. It looked and felt as if the doors had closed for us, because the planning cycles for school finances were so long and precarious.

There is a long-term follow-up anecdote to this initial but solitary success, however. About 10 years later, long after I had left medical practice and was working internationally full time to spread this preventive method, I was walking along the main shopping street of our town and had to step aside around half a dozen young men in their early twenties who were talking in an animated fashion in the middle of the pavement. One, a huge, tall guy, saw me and looked intently at me. He stepped away from the group and said, pointing a finger, 'Are you Dr Griffiths?' There was something in his posture that was slightly intimidating, so I cautiously replied that I was, anticipating some trouble. His response floored me. 'Emotional Logic, was it?' I nodded. 'I want to thank you! You turned my life around. I was a mess at that school, but it all made so much sense after that.' We had a very pleasant five-minute conversation, and then life moved on.

It was in that community college that the teachers impressed upon me how important it was to teach Emotional Logic to children before the transition to secondary school. 'If a child has problems at transition, they have problems for a lifetime,' I was told. The life transition between schools, I came to acknowledge, majorly disrupts friendships, life habits and safe places. It happens at an age where learning is rapidly embedded into brain structure and future anticipations, affecting the way people will respond to other major life transitions and challenges later, such as employment and redundancy, marriage, childbirth and child rearing responsibilities, ill health or injury. I realised we had to take seriously what the teachers were telling me. We had to normalise grieving as a healthy part of human development for primary school children. However, at that time we had no access to the primaries or other secondary schools.

Preventing problems for transition between schools

At a breakfast meeting in Devon, I met the visiting speakers, the Vice Principal of a secondary academy in Yorkshire, John Bunce and his wife Liz, who was a former infant school Head Teacher and mother of their four teenage children. They talked about the practical and social difficulties of making their move from the south of England into a northern culture. In this new setting, Liz had developed a pastoral support role through a local church, and thus had met Carly, formerly a difficult pupil from that local secondary academy. Carly's life had been highly chaotic. She was well known in the school and local community as someone who had defeated every professional service with her misuse of alcohol and drugs and her promiscuity. She now had two children, both fostered prior to adoption, and she was struggling emotionally. I mentioned to Liz after the meeting that Emotional Logic might help Carly.

We set up a Skype remote-learning session for after their return to Yorkshire. We had only two sessions. I never saw Carly, apart from her dashing out of the room to have a cigarette. In fact, the only reason Carly had agreed to sit in and listen during these Skype sessions was that I had said we did not need to look backwards at any troubles in her past, only consider how Emotional Logic might change things now and looking forwards. This broke the initial barrier, because she had become annoyed and uncooperative with other supports or agencies who had repeatedly asked her to retell the story of her early troubles. This only re-shocked her, which made her feel even worse. But Liz learnt enough about Shock, safe places and Bargaining styles to apply the basics of the healthy adjustment process to managing a practical problem that Carly was facing.

Carly had a part-time voluntary role in a charity office. She was running into conflict with a staff member – yet again. Liz and Carly agreed after the first Skype call to explore an assertive alternative to her normally aggressive style of Bargaining – and it worked! To Carly's amazement, the situation had evolved into something unexpectedly good. That opened a door to her making renewed attempts at exploring alternative responses, with Liz as her emotionally available safe place. Cutting a long and occasionally bumpy story short, Carly eventually recovered the care of one child, married, settled into a job, and reconciled with significant people from her formerly difficult past. Along the way, however, within just of few days of that first change of attitude, people had started noticing a difference.

'What's happened to Carly?' they were asking. The academy leadership noticed. Decisions were made. Emotional Logic was taught to some teaching and pastoral staff. Benefits resulted in various features of children's behaviour, as shown in the 'Rickter scale' star chart (Figure 14.1), which shows the change from before learning Emotional Logic (blue inner line) to after (red outer line).

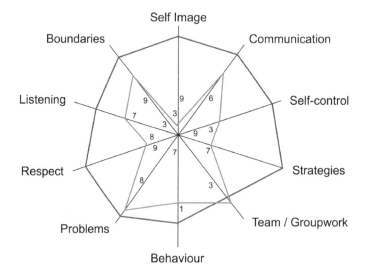

Figure 14.1 – Rickter scale showing change for a teenager learning EL

After learning Emotional Logic, young people had been able to stop self-harming. Suicidal thoughts could be talked about safely, and resolved. Liz was invited to form a new 'inclusion unit' for children at risk of exclusion, where the programme and the content of the rooms were based on the Emotional Logic method. A later Ofsted inspection team interviewed children, parents and staff at that unit and gave it a highly commended status.

The inclusion unit in Plymouth heard about the success, and replicated the system there with equal success. Liz became our Schools Lead. She applied her experience as a former infant school Head Teacher to develop age-appropriate classroom lesson plans that *keep things simple*. They have become the basis of our whole school community programme, which has impacted thousands of children and adults.

The timely arrival of Christiaan Stirling in our Emotional Logic team, a former primary school Head Teacher, enabled the Plymouth inclusion unit to hold meetings that aimed to roll-out the Emotional Logic method more widely to schools in Plymouth, using the class teaching materials that Liz had developed. Via many ups and downs due to political turmoil and funding cuts, Christiaan eventually made an arrangement with the Plymouth Learning Partnership of 67 primary schools and some secondaries to make Emotional Logic's whole-school community programme widely available throughout the city and surrounding areas.

This is the Butterfly Effect at work. A noticeable change in Carly's life from just two learning sessions about a healthy emotional adjustment process led to a large and growing impact. It happened, however, because Carly was able to explore new possibilities while in a stabilising relationship with an emotionally available adult. This is the key issue at the root of Emotional Logic's capacity to prevent mental illness and socially disruptive behaviour, and to promote a strong and exploratory character.

A 'whole-school community' programme means the teachers and staff, the pupils *and* their parents or guardians all, as far as they can, learn to make sense of unpleasant emotions in the same constructive way. The core significance of whole-school community is that education is not only about optimising individual children for exams. It is about how people learn to communicate when facing problems. How can they potentially cooperate to become an adaptive community that includes healthy diversity within a sense of unity? The Emotional Logic method helps to maintain unity where there are differences between people. It involves harnessing people's grief into explicitly naming their *personal values*. Bullying and traumatisation may follow if those values are not named.

Liz and a teacher friend, Zoë, produced first of all a set of lesson plan booklets called *Finding your power and using it* (see Figure 14.2). This provides teachers with six sets of weekly materials for children aged 9-11, preparing them for life, including the transition from primary to secondary schooling.

Figure 14.2 – Cover of *Finding your power and using it*

As mentioned in Chapter 3, the seven icons developed for the 'picture cards' (see page 39) and used throughout *Finding your power and using it* are specifically *not* facial emoticons. This is because there are many children and adults borderline on the autistic spectrum who cannot read facial expressions, so they would not know how to handle the cards to represent their inner emotional worlds. Instead, the icons all have some sort of *movement* represented.

Movement connects with the core medical understanding of emotions – as physical preparations for action towards, or movement away from, changing situations (E-motion = energy in motion). Young people, and many adults also, make sense of their feelings of emotion by handling the picture cards and other materials *kinaesthetically*, moving them physically and then connecting the names of the emotions to their memories of how they felt in different situations. They thus can learn the useful purposes of feelings that are now more clearly recognised. Because their learning brains are already primed by handling the cards and materials to be active and exploratory, they learn to become active agents over those named emotional energies, not passive victims of them. This enhances the sense of personal identity. Self-respect and empowerment rapidly grow to influence relationships reasonably, without trying to control others.

When Christian joined the team, he became joint Schools Lead with Liz. Together they developed more materials for younger age groups. *The Talking Together Tree* emerged as a story told by teachers to children aged 4-7 (Figure 14.3).

Figure 14.3 – Cover of *The Talking Together Tree*

Figure 14.4 (a) and (b) – Examples of Talking Together Trees

Teachers would set the children to make models or wall charts on which dangled leaves that represented emotions and their useful purposes. One example of the impact among many is a 5-year-old boy who took a leaf from the tree up to the teacher's table and said, 'I would like to tell the class why I am feeling angry'. Imagine the lifelong impact of such a youngster not needing to act out his anger to control his classmates' attention...

Further work led to *Doctor in the House*, designed to fill the gap for 7–9 year-olds so that revision could follow every two years with age-appropriate variations that matched the school curriculum. A sample of two of the pages is shown in Figure 14.5.

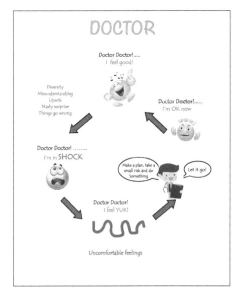

Figure 14.5 (a) and (b) – Two pages from *Doctor in the House*

While this was happening, I was following up an idea from a psychologist and teacher in South Africa, Reinet, to produce a series of illustrated children's story books in which Savannah animals represent the seven core adjustment emotions. These are the books that feature in Chapter 9. I worked with various teachers to pitch the language for 6-10 year olds, and by engaging a professional illustrator, *Shelly and Friends* was born (see Figure 14.6). The stories show how emotions can cooperate, like a group of friends, to solve everyday problems. The series was designed for a

Figure 14.6 – *The Shelly and Friends* series

parent or other adult to read the books first to the children, and to set them going with creative activities to encourage healthy expression of emotions.

We received numerous reports of children identifying closely with Shelly the tortoise, who hides in her shell when scared or hurt and doesn't know how to come out again, and likewise with Reggie and Zora, to learn how their angry or guilty feelings respectively have useful purposes. One child would take the Shelly book to a garden shed whenever she was feeling anxious, and come out transformed each time. Such is the learning process. The parents learnt simultaneously, and some grandparents. Teachers love them.

One of the problems with preventive work is that measuring impact is so difficult when many variables affect a desired outcome. Helping young people to cope better with the stresses of transition to secondary school is hard to compare numerically between groups who do or do not have the learning intervention. Significantly, the aim of this type of preventive work is not just to make that transition less stressful. It is to equip young people with a method of resilience and adaptability that they can *choose* to use appropriately in any and every stressful situation they encounter for the rest of their lives. When the method becomes a normal part of daily conversations, the skills cascade further through families, neighbourhoods and organisations. That is a successful outcome from our point of view, when a whole-school community approach leads to adaptive inner transformation and inner strength. The impact is subtle. It takes an unpredictable period of time, so standard research protocols to measure change do not work.

An excellent example of a successful outcome comes from the story of what happened at a local grammar school. At the initial Plymouth inclusion unit roll-out meeting with Christiaan were the Vice Principal (VP) for pastoral care and an attendance officer at this school who had been impressed with the potential. The school Principal gave full support for the VP and attendance officer to join a two-term course to qualify at a level we now call an Emotional Logic Facilitator – an ELF. (Teachers were falling over themselves wanting to become the school's ELF!) The ELF was qualified to train other teachers and staff to deliver the school lesson plans, and to have one-to-one coaching conversations with children who were struggling, and with their parents. Having a trained ELF meant that a school could sustain the presence of Emotional Logic skills even when there was staff turnover.

Having qualified, the VP then organised roll-out training for the 30 teachers and pastoral staff who might be most involved with the Year 7 new intake of pupils.

The training was run by herself and the attendance officer, supported by Christiaan to consolidate their Emotional Logic training skills. The new intake of pupils in September received the six lessons in their Personal, Social and Health Education curriculum slots (PSHE) over the first two terms. During this time, I worked with the attendance officer, guiding her to use the class lesson plans as a helpful structure for her small family group talks with children and parents who had attendance problems. The materials empowered and released her to discover the issues, values and worries that were influencing school attendance.

A transformation was immediately obvious. The Principal was so impressed that he altered the pattern with which the teachers for the entry years took on new classes, ensuring that those who taught Year 7 intake classes all had high Emotional Logic skill levels. Meanwhile, the VP had rolled out training to the pastoral staff for all the school Years, had run parents' evenings, and had trained peer supporters. In that second year, a 42% reduction in reported cases of aggressive behaviour was recorded.

The attendance officer became more confident with the method, and such was her success at turning around school anxieties that her reputation spread among the parents. Several started seeing her to help resolve their own relationship problems that they felt were affecting their children. The perception of her role by parents changed from being 'like a police officer', to being a helper. This is the perfect picture of a whole-school community approach to teaching Emotional Logic. Teaching staff, children in classes, parents and peer supporters all discovered that the language of Emotional Logic made adjustments and adaptability less stressful.

Another example outside the school system will be helpful to explain the unpredictable personal development that can follow equipping *relationships* with the language of Emotional Logic. A charitable project working with difficult-to-engage families used the Shelly book series to help both the parents and the children to understand their emotional worlds better. The mothers met as a learning club in a garden with two facilitators to read the books in parallel with other materials. As they understood the overall adjustment process, they became motivated to read the books to their children. On our YouTube Channel – Emotional Logic Centre – there were recorded readings of the seven stories. So, if the parents were not confident to read, they could nevertheless listen together and stay with their children while they turned the pages to look and learn. The results have been uplifting. Children previously withdrawn or angry and confrontational started talking about feelings that their parents never imagined they were experiencing. Mutual responsiveness improved.

Two comments from mums were enlightening: 'I feel as if I have gone through life with my eyes shut. Now it all makes so much sense'; 'People tell us these emotions are negative, but they all have useful purposes!' One of the children who was school refusing, moved to a new school and discovered how enjoyable it was.

The stories go on and on. They all follow from, 'What's happened to Carly?!' Adaptive transformation of life takes time, but inner strength grows if people start to respect each other's grief emotions as evidence of their personal values. This second strand would be incomplete, however, without mentioning finally another area of great significance.

Reinet, as mentioned before, is a counselling psychologist in Pretoria, South Africa, who qualified as an Emotional Logic tutor and was the original inspiration for the *Shelly and Friends* book series. After herself having a child on the autistic spectrum, she established a small school for children with high-functioning autistic spectrum difficulties, realising that the standard approach to schooling simply would not work where the children had such unique patterns of sensory overload and language barriers. She knew from her own home, however, that they also could have rich emotional worlds, but be 'expressively locked in' and unable to communicate them. She was highly imaginative in her individualising of creative kinaesthetic learning methods

Figure 14.7 – Picture cards laid out by a pupil at Reinet's school

appropriate to each child. Her unique school integrates Emotional Logic daily into the curriculum, and she has found that it vastly reduces the frequency and length of emotional melt-downs – the equivalent of the finding in that example grammar school of reduced aggressive behaviour.

Each student develops their unique representations of the seven emotional Stepping Stones cards. They thus *know* how to show, 'This is how it feels!' For example, a 9-year-old girl with an Asperger's personality laid out the cards shown in Figure 14.7. Her father is also on the spectrum and battled to show emotions. He simply found it too overwhelming to hug. In Reinet's words, 'Our student is a sensory seeker, with a love language of touch. So it felt like Dad was not being there for her. She shared this card pattern and was so happy to be able to show Dad how she felt. It was wonderful to see the hope in her. We worked at other ways of feeling loved by Dad. They now take walks together and both look after her pet bearded dragon.'

Reinet won a contract with Gauteng Province's Department for Education to teach Emotional Logic to the teachers at eight failing township schools, with a view to improving educational performance in the children. She started wondering whether her work had had any impact, so she decided to return two years later to one of them. As she approached the school she stopped in her tracks, and took the photograph shown in Figure 14.8. On the outside of the wall facing the local community someone, or some class, had painted three of the Emotional Logic icons. Now that, we agreed, is an example of whole school community impact.

14.8 – Photograph of community school painting of EL icons

A new understanding of mental health for schools

For over three decades in the UK, the notion of an individual's *mental health* and their *mental illness* have held sway among professional services as a main focus for interventions. In Europe, Africa and Asia, however, there is a far more widespread appreciation of social factors impacting an individual's wellbeing. The term *psychosocial health* is equivalent in those cultures to *mental health* in the highly individualised UK.

School teachers in the UK are increasingly expected to be able to promote the mental health of their pupils. However, they are disempowered from doing so by the way they have to interface with a healthcare system that is grounded in individualism. Psychology services generally need a mental illness *diagnosis* for an individual before embarking on a course of therapy or treatment. This means that services that inreach to schools, such as mental Health First Aid training, tend to focus on recognising illness and early diagnosis. This disempowers teachers, who feel that as soon as a mental illness diagnosis is made they have no training to intervene. A further complication follows, that the diagnostic model involves two waiting lists – firstly the referral for assessment and diagnosis, then a second one to begin a treatment plan, usually with a different care professional who needs to start all over again with getting to know this individual. Remember Carly. Teachers remain disempowered while a pupil is on these waiting lists. Very often, the referral is rejected by the overworked mental health services, who cannot cope with so many 'early diagnoses'.

Emotional Logic, by contrast, is grounded in a view of the person as social and ecological. By definition, a person is an individual 'of a people in an environment'. The term *person* is part of the same group of ideas as parent, sister, cousin, employee, citizen, friend, etc. All of these are intrinsically relational. There has to be 'an other' for any of these terms to mean anything. To be a citizen, for example, there has to be a state. To be a pupil, there has to be a teacher in a school environment. To be a whole person, there must be responsive others. A whole person is incomplete alone.

Emotional Logic equips people to be responsive to each other. It takes a medical view of emotions as 'social physiology' – as physical preparations for action or withdrawal in shared social environments. By contrast with the individualistic view of mental illness, Emotional Logic understands *personal development* as the way to promote mental health and prevent mental illness. The lifelong-learning method of Emotional Logic is one that re-empowers teachers in *their* professional role and environment to teach about healthy relationship dynamics. It adds insight to behaviours, by giving people the capacity to name their personal values and those of others in the whole-school community.

A far better long-term aim for educators would be to leave behind that individualist mental paradigm, and to aim instead to equip generations of emotionally responsive citizens, neighbours and family members.

The growing awareness among mental health professionals in the UK of the impact of trauma-induced grief on personal development is at last beginning to shift professional thinking away from a need to diagnose mental illness to initiate therapy plans. This new emphasis on the traumatic psychosocial nature of emotional development lags behind the rest of the world, however. We had the good fortune to develop much of Emotional Logic's practical work in environments abroad that already were trauma-informed – in Russia, Zimbabwe and South Africa. It was first taught in South Africa as an optional module on trauma management, as part of a psychology degree course.

The need now is for teachers in the UK to activate *their own* Emotional Logic for mutual support, first in the school's staff room and their homes. Then, even when having to discipline pupil bad behaviour or manage their poor achievement, teachers might still be emotionally available to pupils and their parents to help them manage loss constructively.

Imagine a school in which Emotional Logic was taught as a core curriculum subject on healthy adaptability alongside English (or any local language) and Maths. The pieces of the jigsaw are all there. They just need putting together.

Chapter 15

It's never too late
– the Revival Choir

Sandy was in her fifties or sixties, with snow-white hair and a beautiful smile that readily lit up her face as she turned to greet you. She and her husband David were a strong but gentle presence of peace who moved easily among a church congregation, knowing everyone as if they were family. This particular non-conformist fellowship had decided to have all their pastoral leaders trained in Emotional Logic, and that included Sandy and Dave.

Apart from leading a mid-week home group, where church attendees from all backgrounds grew to know each other better, Sandy also had a heart for the older members of the church, the widowed and widowers. She ran a morning group for about a dozen in their seventies and eighties. It was an 'all-generation' church fellowship, from babes-in-arms to these wise seniors, who might at times be surrogate grandparents to the exhausted middle generation's noisy and playful children.

Sandy was quick to grasp the idea that our unpleasant emotions have useful purposes. She found the idea liberating, especially when so many churches speak negatively about emotions, which she had always thought was odd when so much of life was meant to be about love. She wanted to share this new understanding widely, and see how others took to it.

So it came about that Sandy passed on what she knew to the Senior's Group, and shared the handouts, thinking that they might like to talk about how life changes for them as they get that bit older. To her surprise, a number of them felt the same sort of liberation of spirit that she had experienced. They particularly commented, she told me later, on a sense of relief that anger was not criticised, but presented instead as a passion for life, to go out despite danger and prevent the loss of something important. It seemed that not only here, but in many churches, anger was looked on as a sign of bad or weak character.

What happened next was totally unexpected. One of the seniors started talking about her Second World War experience, and the latent shock and anger that she still felt about that, 60 years on. It gave others a sense of permission to talk about their residual emotions from that terrible time. And the floodgates opened. People started talking about things they had never shared with anyone before. Honesty was welcomed and greeted with understanding. A closeness grew, and comfort grew in equal measure to the frustration and hurt expressed.

Apparently, this new level of openness continued from week to week, and with it camaraderie and good humour grew. Sandy was delighted that their lives seemed transfigured. Someone asked her what they should do with all this new energy, which started a discussion. Ideas were thrown around, and thus was born the Revival Choir. With rehearsals, a purpose, and gusto, they took themselves to the front on a Sunday morning, and sang to the church.

*

This story always makes us chuckle whenever we think of it. Emotional Logic liberates our humanity to explore its fullest potential. Forming a choir and standing up to perform was like a mini-resurrection.

Community choirs have sprung up everywhere since then. People from every background and culture could enjoy their ability to share and aspire to something more together. To young people, the Seniors Group in the church might previously have seemed like some elderly folk looking towards their end, but at the front they turned around. They took a deep breath and sang to the young from their new-found bonds as a choir. The young listened, and something of the seniors' renewed energy for life was visible, almost tangible.

Twice I, Trevor, have sung in a large 'people's choir' production of Handel's Messiah, joining the four-part harmonies where volume drowns my imperfections. Feeling the reverberation in my own chest of the voices of my neighbours is an uplifting experience, perhaps the closest to heaven that I could have on earth. As part of singing in an amateur choir, it helps to listen to your neighbours to work out if either you or they are slightly off pitch. There is something about mutual awareness in such a context that, to me, seems to connect into the very source of life. Careful listening is a feature of dynamic relatedness, not passivity. It connects actively with a sense of belonging in something bigger than we can imagine through and beyond the now, which is a handy way to summarise a feature of life that many people call their spirituality.

As a doctor I have had to reflect on how differently people perceive their mortality, and the spirituality associated with that. I think that as many people as there are in the world, there are that many nuances of belief about mortality and death. It is about connection and disconnection – relatedness ending or possibly in transition – so my inclusive, non-divisive way to describe spirituality is 'who you tend to listen to'.

When listening to other people, and in hoping that others will recall someone's words and works after they die, many people do not feel a need to call this listening feature of life spiritual. When people talk of listening to nature, or listening to your own body, the notion of spiritual movement starts to seem more relevant, and in some cultures listening to the wisdom of ancestors certainly is. There is no need to criticise people for whom they listen to, but if we remain respectfully curious, then we can in Emotional Logic terms measure their relatedness against love or compassion, and notice how much grief that love is generating, and if love's many loss emotions are worked out constructively into the social fabric of life. Some people listen to signs in the revolving cosmos or Creation to guide their paths, while others feel they can hear the heart of the Creator as its Source of Life, either inspirationally, or recorded and passed on through a Book to be read and considered. These are all types of personal responsiveness that have their place within a view of spirituality as 'who you tend to listen to'.

Emotional Logic is ultimately a conversational life skill that empowers people to listen to the hurts, and to harness loss emotions into constructive compassion. When I think again of the young people who were listening to the Revival Choir, I am reminded that most of my younger patients rarely gave a thought to their own mortality. A friend of mine sold life insurance for a time. He said ruefully that he was convinced most of his potential clients believed they were never going to die, so insuring against it seemed unreasonable! But could there be any advantage in making our peace early on with the fact of our mortality? True Acceptance in Emotional Logic terms includes both sadness on letting go, *and* a willingness to explore something totally new if an unexpected possibility to renew life arises.

That is the discovery that enlivened the Revival Choir members. It was not a Denial of death that made them sing. It was by activating a full Growth Cycle (see page 12) to explore life again, once they had learnt to share openly and emotionally. Activation like that leads to mature joy. Denial may be a necessary state for many living in difficult circumstances for survival, but if relational safe places do emerge in time, then conversational listening and responding can help life to open up again.

Without that full Growth Cycle view of Acceptance of our mortality making each day precious, people will be forced back onto earlier emotional Stepping Stones as they try to adjust to new stresses. Being Shocked on realising their mortality can leave people stunned and numb and unable to respond when others need comforting. I have known people cross over to the opposite side of a street to avoid encountering a former friend who had been bereaved. Self-doubt can be overcome, however, if the place of decision in a Growth Cycle is acknowledged to feel like emptiness and powerlessness. Surely, that is the perfect place emotionally to be if you are to meet with a friend who is bereaved and feeling that way even more than you do. Who do we listen to?

Some people get angry when recognising their mortality, challenging life with daredevil acts to keep adrenaline flowing, regardless of who clears up any mess left behind. Others turn inwards to question themselves, hoping that good acts will redeem them in the bigger scheme of life. As we try to control life in these ways, who are we listening to?

Some people endlessly Bargain with life, and never let go of the slightest thing even when faced with impossible circumstances. In excess it can lead to greed, envy, isolation of heart and attempts to dominate. Others let go too easily, and never find the courage to Bargain effectively when faced with risk. But at the creative heart of assertive Bargaining is listening carefully to others. And likewise at the heart of *assertively Accepting* that life is not perfect is the hope that life can be ever-renewed. This is not a vain hope, because order *can* re-emerge from chaos after loss. We just have to stay with it long enough for our presence to feed back into it. Perhaps that is what prayer is, and meditation, and thoughtful contemplation? Emotional Logic shows how love's two modes of joy and grief both connect with hope.

Furthermore, some people, on seeing the futility of life, generalise their feelings of emptiness and powerlessness into despair and pointlessness. Who have they been listening to? I think there is a word that has become very unpopular in post-modern society, where the label depression is overused instead. If these states are about seeing our limits in everyday situations, so that we can choose then how to explore our limits, what is now called depression is in fact the misnamed state that used to be called *humility*. It is not only a place of decision, about how we respond to the potential loss of something valued. It is also a place of decision about who we tend to listen to.

Emotional Logic strengthens the inner heart of a person to restore the social responsiveness of love in both of its modes, in joy and in grief, to sustain connection during times of change, disappointment, setback and hurt. If our capacity to listen to others grows, and we choose life having recognised our own mortality, then considering a choir in all its diversity shows how our voices may be heard in unity. That way, life can be ever-renewed.

Appendix

- Common whirlpools of loss emotions
- Naming Feelings lists to transform life
- Published evidence
- Our further learning pathway
- Other learning options
- Shelly and Friends Learning Clubs

Common whirlpools of loss emotions

Several common whirlpools of loss emotions have been described in the chapters. The healthy adjustment process can twist around on itself, so that people end up grieving about the fact that they are grieving. The summary opposite shows, for example, how we can see when some people feel shocked about their guilty feelings, and guilty about how they feel so shocked, going round and round these states until they merge into a sense of shame. When that happens, neither of the adjustment emotions can fulfil its useful purpose to help this person to respond constructively to a named loss. The list shows how distress (withdrawal), tension (irrational action) or confusion can result from different pairs of emotions becoming entangled.

The listed symptoms or drives on the left of this diagram are *not* an inevitable consequence of the two physical emotions shown complicating each other. This information sheet works the other way around. If you encounter someone who has any of those symptoms, they probably have those two emotions entangling. Therefore, learning to harness their useful purposes separately to adjust to a named loss will help to break up that whirlpool.

Clinical depression can result when people flit between various whirlpools that entangle the Depression of loss. Clinical anxiety can result when people flit between various whirlpools that entangle their Shock with other loss emotions. Compulsive behaviour comes from a different whirlpool of Anger entangling with Guilty self-questioning. The stories explain how these whirlpools can untangle themselves when people understand the healthy adjustment process better, and start naming their hidden losses as a normal part of everyday living. After all, this *is* the best way to recognise that you have values, and to work out what other people's values are as well.

Figure A.1

Grieving about my grief

Behaviours and emotional states that emerge from whirlpools of loss emotions

When a person experiences two emotional 'Stepping Stones' of grieving *at the same time*, neither can prepare him or her to fulfil their useful purposes. They generate distress or tension deep within.

<u>Shame</u>   (Withdrawal: in-in)
      Ashamed
      Suspicious
      Paranoid thoughts (+ Anger)

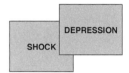

<u>Fatigue</u>   (Withdrawal: in-in)
      Sudden bouts of fatigue
      Recurrent Illness
      Chronic Fatigue Syndrome
      Suppressed immunity

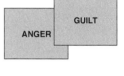

<u>Compulsive Behaviour</u>   (Irrational Action: out-in)
      Perfectionist
      Obsessive Compulsive behaviour
      Impulsive or 'driven' behaviour
      Self harming
      Bulimia

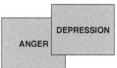

<u>Destructive Behaviour</u>   (Irrational Action: out-in)
      Confrontational
      Vandalism & violent drives
      Obstructive
      Suicidal thoughts

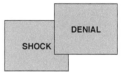

<u>Post Traumatic Stress Disorder</u>   (Confusion: in-out)
      Brittle
      Stressed
      Anxious
      Fearful
      Self-doubting

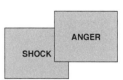

<u>Feeling 'odd and out of it'</u>   (Confusion: in-out)
      Unable to think clearly
      Depersonalisation
      Distanced from life

<u>Low self-regard</u>   (The root of clinical depression: in-in)
      Ruminating
      Self-critical
      Unable to feel pleasure (anhedonia)
      Hopeless

Naming Feelings lists help to transform life

Seven lists of 16 feelings words correspond to each of the seven emotional Stepping Stones for healthy adjustment. Take a pencil, and ring or tick those that you recognise you tend to do in life generally. Then check across to the meanings and useful purposes of each emotional Stepping Stone (see Chapter 2). These may now make more sense of your unique range of feelings when you face the need to make an adjustment in life.

Gaining an improved sense of inner order can strengthen people's self-worth when they feel pressured or stressed. They can then compare and contrast different viewpoints with others about their feelings and emotions.

The first set of four lists includes Shock, Denial, Anger and Guilt – in other words the Stress Cycle.

Figure A.2 (opposite) – Feelings words for
(a) Shock
(b) Denial
(c) Anger
(d) Guilt

(a)

numb	fearful
shaken	apprehensive
anxious	dread
overwhelmed	scared
disorientated	paralysed
confused	panicky
unprepared	trembly
cold sweat	stunned

....

....

(b)

ignore it	disclaim
reject	turn away
invalidate	detach
turn a deaf ear	forget it
refuse to believe	carry on
say it's irrelevant	dismiss
evade	disallow
avoid	disown

....

....

(c)

resentful	bad-tempered
bitter	jealous
irritated	spiteful
furious	frustrated
indignant	wanting revenge
offended	malice
touchy	full of hate
sulky	hold a grudge

....

....

(d)

remorse	repentant
blame	want to own up
my fault	soul searching
flawed	self-questioning
full of regret	should do more
mortified	liable
self reproach	if only
disillusioned	bad conscience

....

....

The second set of three lists includes the three styles of Bargaining, then the Depression of loss, and true Acceptance – in other words, the Growth Cycle.

grab	ask "what if"	am resigned
barge	ask "if... then..."	lie low
feud	endure	wait and see
threaten	negotiate	stagnate
pursue a vendetta	risk	play dead
	motivate	concede
corner	convince	turn shy
poison	inspire	submit
dominate	try	step back
put down	declare	hesitate
oppress	influence	apathetic
drive others	take turns	non-action
force	be present	accept defeat
break	write a letter	get nostalgic
pressure	team up	acquiesce
bully	offer	be moulded

Figure A.3 – The three styles of Bargaining

Figure A.4 – Feelings words for
(a) Depression of loss
(b) True Acceptance

(a)

suppressed	subdued
hopeless	powerless
miserable	ineffective
useless	sick at heart
feel defeated	flat
despair	empty
care worn	worthless
dispirited	pointless

(b)

hope	gentleness
integrity	liberation
joy	serenity
self-control	maturity
forgiveness	resolved
grace	sadness
healing	relief
moved on	peace

We also show the wall posters that are used in some school classrooms.

Schools Naming Feelings posters

Numb
Stuck
Shaken
Anxious
Fearful
It's too much
Confused
Jolted
Restless
Unprepared
Scared
In a flap
Surprised
Alarmed
Dread
The jitters
Trembly
Panic
Terror
Out of control
Stunned

Shock

Ignore it
Reject it
Withdraw
Dismiss
Turn away
Keep to self
Refuse to believe
Forget it
Turn a deaf ear
Withhold
It's not possible
Doesn't matter
Shut off
Avoid
I will talk about it later

Denial

Angry
Resentful
Bitter
Wound up
Furious
Offended
Get my own back
Rival
Adrenaline
Bad temper
Rage
Passion
Envy
Spite
Rush
Hate
Frustrated
Have a grudge
Hostile

Anger

On my mind
Regret
What happened?
Soul searching
Question myself
It's always me
Blame
If only...
What did I do?
Go over and over it
Curious
It's my fault
Feeling guilty

Guilt

Bargaining

Endure
Don't give up
Convince
Try again
Take Turns
Be present
Ask"what if?"
Team up
Persuade

Grab
Barge
Make threats
Insult
Force
Pressure others
Bully
Break

Lie low
Hide
Wait and see
Turn shy
Give in
Hesitate
Accept defeat
Keep quiet
Surrender

Depression

Hopeless
Invisible
Feel defeated
I'm worthless
Flat
Empty
Powerless
Low
Useless
Despair
Rubbish
Miserable
No energy
Dull
Pointless
No joy
Heavy heart
Sad
Shut off
Sluggish
Tired for ages

Acceptance

Hopeful
Peace
In control of myself
Chilled
Let go of the past
More free
Wiser head
Sorted
Bit sad but it's ok
Settled
Looking forward
Relief
Feel better about me
Moving on
Showing joy

Schools Naming Feelings posters

Another of the wall posters used in schools is 'How's your Bargaining'. This may be put up in school corridors. Then, if two people are getting into an argument a staff member can take them to this poster and turn the incident into a learning opportunity.

How's your Bargaining?

Bargaining is what we do to get something back which matters to us. How do you go about it?

Aggressive	Assertive	Passive
Grab	Endure	Lie low
Barge	Don't give up	Hide
Make threats	Convince	Wait and see
Insult	Try again	Turn shy
Force	Take turns	Give in
Pressure others	Be present	Hesitate
Bully	Ask "what if?"	Accept defeat
Break	Team up	Keep quiet
	Persuade	Surrender
Watch out for consequences or secondary losses!	It takes courage and determination to try these but they are effective ways to recover a loss	Watch out for consequences or secondary losses!

Published evidence

If any reader is interested to see copies of these papers, please email: office@emotionallogicentre.org.uk.

Griffiths T. Preventing alienation and social disorder with 'Emotional Logic'. *Safer Communities* 2013; 12(2): 79-85.

Zahra D, Langsford M, Griffiths T. Emotional logic development profiles – validating the benefits and safety of emotional logic training. *International Journal of Psychiatry in Clinical Practice* 2016; 20(3): 141-145. DOI: 10.1080/13651501.2016.1197270

Turton A, Langsford M, Di Lorenzo D, et al. An audit of emotional logic for mental health self-care improving social connection. *European Journal of Integrative Medicine* 2020; 37: 101167. DOI: 10.1016/j.eujim.2020.101167

Langsford M, Griffiths T. Learning and teaching Emotional Logic in Zimbabwe: A lifelong learning emotional literacy training package that promotes healthy adjustment in resource-poor settings. *Tropical Doctor* 2015; 45: 158-163. DOI:10.1177/0049475515577525

Stirling C, Bunce E, Griffiths T. Olivia's Story: Emotional Logic as a Systemic Lifelong-learning Intervention for Adaptability. *Context* August 2018.

Griffiths T. *Lost and Then Found: Turning Life's Disappointments into Hidden Treasures*. 1999: Paternoster.

Our further learning pathway

Online Introductory Course

Nine 3-8 minute videos and supporting documents to give an overview of the healthy adjustment process in 1-2 evenings. Gain access to our **online emotion-mapping tools site** to share your understanding with others. An ideal introduction for family or friends to start helpful conversations. Watch also with several people in a small organisation to decide if further learning would be helpful.

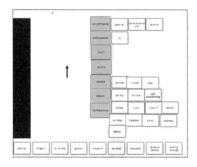

Foundation Award 2021

For personal development to qualify in eight weeks with a full understanding of the healthy process of adjustment to change, setbacks, disappointments and hurts. Four live webinars develop your conversational skills. Share your new understanding to benefit family, friends and colleagues. RQLE Accreditation with the University of Surrey for CPD.

General Coaching Award 2021

A casework supervision module following the Foundation Award. Learn how to guide other people's self-help learning to untangle more complex life problems. Integrate the Emotional Logic method into your existing work practices, or become a self-employed sole trader, franchised as an EL Coach. For support workers and person-

EL Facilitator Award – Schools

(Become your school's ELF!)

Learn to train teachers and pastoral staff how to use Emotional Logic for their own inner strengthening, and to use six lesson plans to introduce EL to the pupils. Learn our 'safe coaching method' to work with individual pupils and/or parents to resolve behavioural, attendance and academic performance problems. Prevent mental illness and disruptive behaviour using a whole school community approach.

Business and Leadership option: Courses and personalised business coaching training

A range of programmes are run by Chris Lorimer through our partner organisation, the **Devon Business and Education Centre (DBEC)** and at other venues. Apply foundational principles of adaptability to transform work-life balance with inner strength, and develop corporate performance, team responsiveness and workforce wellness.

Other learning options

Personal Learning Appointment

Remote learning by Zoom, or face-to-face, 30-90 minutes. For individuals, couples, friends, or small family groups learning together to improve conversational and adaptability skills, and to gain inner strength.

Family Learning Pack

Shelly and Friends hard copy set of seven illustrated children's books for ages 6 to 10. Four sets of emotion cards, and four sets of feelings cards. 'Don't tell me how you feel; use these cards to show me how you feel.' Plus an Activity Pack for adults and older children to share and learn how to adjust and adapt constructively when facing change, disappointments, setbacks and hurts.

Enquire at:
hello@emotionallogiccentre.org.uk, or +44(0)1752 892455
Buy from:
elcentre.org/shop

Shelly and Friends Learning Clubs

The *Shelly and Friends* illustrated book series can provide quality time for parents, grandparents, and child-minders to spend with children aged 5 to 10. We run online learning clubs for the adults so that they can learn for themselves the healthy adjustment process, and help their children to see how the seven stories fit together.

SHELLY IN SHOCK
A sudden problem means the Savannah friends have to change where they play. With the help of wise Lisimba the lion, Shelly and her friends learn that shock can be very useful.

OLLIE IN DENIAL
It's the annual Savannah Carnival parade. But Ollie the ostrich has a problem getting there... and he doesn't want to think about it!

REGGIE GETS ANGRY
Reggie the Rhino has a bit of a temper. In fact sometimes he becomes ENRAGED! But being angry about things is perfectly normal. Find out how Reggie's anger is useful in a good way.

ZORA FEELS GUILTY
Zora sees everything in black and white. But when she makes a mistake, she discovers that her friends can add more colour and fun to learning how to do things better next time.

MONTE RISKS A BARGAIN
Monte has hidden some food in a hollow by some rocks, but when Esther the elephant returns from a long journey to see her relatives, she falls asleep on top of it. Monte discovers there is more than one way to try to move a mountain...

ESTHER FEELS EMPTY
Esther loves being the wise helper for her friends, but when a drought comes and her friends leave to find food, she feels empty and powerless and very low. Lisimba the wise lion helps her to see how even this can help her to grow wiser when she learns how to live patiently. Together they look for new opportunities to explore.

GEMMIE ACCEPTS THE LONG VIEW
The friends decide to throw a secret birthday party for Lisimba. They all agree; but how to do it makes them all disagree! They discover that honestly sharing their emotions helps them to find a new way all to pull together. And so they discover the joy of life again, together in the Savannah.

Index